MW00583961

PETROLEUM RESEARCH AND
VENEZUELA'S INTEVEP

THE
CLASH
OF
THE
GIANTS

PETROLEUM RESEARCH AND VENEZUELA'S INTEVEP

THE CLASH OF THE GIANTS

BY

EMMA BROSSARD, PH.D.

HOUSTON, TEXAS
1993

Copyright © 1993 by INTEVEP

Library of Congress Cataloging-in-publications

Brossard, E.B.
Petroleum research and Venezuela's INTEVEP:
the clash of the giants / by Emma Brossard.
p.   cm.
Includes index.
ISBN 0-87814-399-8

1. Petroleum industry and trade — Venezuela —
History. 2. INTEVEP, S.A. — History.
3. Petroleum — Research — Venezuela —
History.

I. Title
HD9574, V42B76   1993
338.2'7282'0987 — dc20   93-13661
                                                 CIP

This book
is dedicated
to the
Founders and
Researchers
of Intevep.

TABLE OF CONTENTS

CHAPTER I

CHAPTER II

CHAPTER III

CHAPTER IV

CHAPTER V

CHAPTER VI

ACKNOWLEDGMENTS

D eep gratitude is acknowledged for time spent in interviews, follow-up information and clarifications to all at Intevep, to others within the Venezuelan oil industry, and to the distinguished founders of Invepet and Intevep. I am also grateful to the executives and researchers of Shell Development Co. and Exxon Production Research Co. in Houston, who met with me and supplied information for the first chapter.

Among all of these helpful and informative people, a few spent considerable time informing me and correcting my work. Dr. Nestor Barroeta, Vice President of Intevep, was my primary guide and teacher. He opened the doors to see the Founders, and many executives in the Venezuelan oil industry. Some day he will write his own personal book on Intevep, as he has been there from the beginning, having arrived with his "IVIC group" of researchers.

Alejandro Villoria was my cheerful guide through so many facets of the founding period. On my many trips to Intevep, he also showed me around the institute that he lovingly helped to found, for he was at Invepet in Los Ruices, where he successfully pushed and directed the first research program in petroleum products, as Section and Project Manager, and was one of the first to move to Intevep. He now heads Intevep's new offices and labs in Western Venezuela, in Maracaibo.

And there is a special lady at Intevep, who willingly and graciously helped in getting so many interviews, reports, maps, books, articles in newspapers, papers presented at conferences, and encouraged others to send me promised material, that without her help I would have come to a stand still. Elizabeth Segovia, Dr. Barroeta's secretary, was indispensable in writing this book.

■

A book about research, or a book about the petroleum industry is accomplished only with the help of many, and in the end with the help of a few key friends. There is no one in the Venezuelan oil industry today, who has been in as many key posts (President of: Pequiven, Meneven, and Lagoven) after rising through the ranks of Standard Oil/Creole, and who better understands all of the operations and the history of this industry, than Renato Urdaneta. I am very grateful for his careful reading of each of the chapters and for his corrections, suggestions and clarifications. His help was invaluable.

And finally, thank you Gustavo Inciarte, President of Intevep, for asking me to write a book on Intevep. You realized the story of Intevep had to be told, and I'll always be grateful you chose me. I learned about research in the oil industry, about the dedicated scientists and visionaries of my beautiful country — Venezuela — and more about the industry to which I was born.

PREFACE

The international oil industry, dynamic by nature, is currently in the throes of one of the most profound transformations in its history. While confronting the challenges of a new energy era, the oil industry must plan ahead to develop the supplies needed to match demand through the 1990s and beyond.

Dr. Brossard's book shows how this transformation is reshaping the future of Venezuela's longstanding oil industry. This meticulously researched work provides an analytical history of Venezuela's oil industry, and its pioneering efforts in heavy oils and the related production of Orimulsion fuel, as well as a descriptive account of the country's petroleum research establishments.

The book serves a further purpose, in that it examines the response of a key OPEC Member to the new context facing the international oil industry.

Let me begin this preface by briefly stating what, from the point of view of OPEC as a whole, are the main factors constituting this changed context. The principal issues which OPEC, and the world at large, will have to tackle in the coming years are: energy security; the environment; and the need for international producer-consumer cooperation.

These elements are, in fact, intertwined. Thus, energy security is crucial to the economic health of the OECD region and the Newly Industrialized Countries (NICs). The developing world needs energy in order to modernize and diversify it economies. Meanwhile, OPEC Members remain heavily dependent on petroleum revenues, and need secure markets to justify investment in maintaining and increasing their oil production capacity. On the face of it, then, there should be a confluence of interest.

■

The environment issue is likely to have a growing impact on the world oil market. The current decade will witness increasing efforts to get to grips with the accumulated pollution of three centuries of industrial development, and to place economic growth on a sustainable basis. This is a global problem, which cannot be dealt with in a piecemeal fashion. Likewise, petroleum producer-consumer relations urgently require a cooperative approach, without which market stability cannot be attained. A free-for-all would be highly damaging to long-term investment prospects, and thus ultimately, to the interests of North and South alike.

If we accept that the objectives of oil producers and consumers are, indeed, complementary, it follows that resources, information, know-how and technology will have to be shared. For instance, in order to ensure an adequate flow of oil to the consumer, information will need to be exchanged so as to increase the predictability of the supply and demand sides of the equation. And the condition will have to be created for a rapid and massive increase in investment in productive capacity.

While national strategies will inevitably differ, it is safe to say that the student of trends in the international oil market can scarcely ignore the far-sighted and innovative role played by the Venezuelan petroleum industry in recent years. A co-founder and loyal Member of OPEC, the country has taken a balanced approach to the emerging structural changes in world oil that constitutes a highly constructive policy input for our Organization.

Like other producers, Venezuela may well have to face a context of relatively modest increases in oil demand. Depletion of domestic hydrocarbon reserves in the industrial countries, growing dependence on oil imports and environmental concerns have focused international attention on the search for ways to reduce growth in energy demand, to increase the efficiency of energy conversion technology, and to commercialize tech-

■

nologies that tap alternative energy sources. Convergence of these considerations and other factors influencing the global energy mix will determine the long-term demand for oil.

Currently, six OPEC Member Countries account for over 90% of the Organization's total proven oil reserves of 776 billion barrels. In terms of current OPEC production Venezuela ranks fourth, while on the basis of conventional oil reserves, with proven oil reserves of over 62 billion barrels, it ranks sixth after Saudi Arabia (260), Iraq (100), UAE (98), Kuwait (97) and Iran (93). However, considering the country's vast deposits of heavy oil in the Orinoco Belt — recoverable reserves of which are estimated at over 250 billion barrels — Venezuela will no doubt continue to play a key role in shaping the future of world oil and energy prospects.

Dr. Subroto
Secretary General of OPEC
Vienna, Austria
August, 1992

INTRODUCTION

R esearch about research institutes would seem to come at the end of one's career in research and writing. Only then can one appreciate the responsibility of the task of writing a book about men who have tried to conquer nature. The purpose of this book is to formulate the issue of scientific inquiry with the focus on the oil industry in Venezuela. It is an account that begins with the clash of great minds over the founding of a research institute for the Venezuelan petroleum industry. It is a debate that is still going on, even after celebrating its 15-year anniversary, in 1989, and as it approaches its 20-year anniversary.

To those unfamiliar with the great debates of the Ancients and the Moderns, it may seem merely a new debate of ideas. However, it is the same debate of the Ancient Greeks, i.e., between philosophers over the question of developing technology. The Moderns opted for developing technology, and since then the debates are more intense because we enjoy the benefits and pay the price for technology. The issue between antiquity and modernity is not between eras but between alternative views of man and his surroundings.

> Men to whom the truths are merely presented remain in twilight. Men who are led or compelled to repeat in themselves the generation of the truth possess it as others cannot.[1]

The power of science is the power of man, therefore, the knowledge about man takes precedence over the scientific accomplishments of man.

---

[1] Joseph Cropsey, ed., Ancients and Moderns, Essays in Honor of Leo Strauss (New York: Basic Books, 1964), p. ix

The power of man is a power to procure human good or ill, therefore, nature must be discovered. Francis Bacon believed that nature was at its truest when "vexed" and "tortured" by experiments. Like Machiavelli, Bacon was a hedonist. Bacon believed that the things that have made men grateful are those that have "relieved man's estate" — i.e., inventions. By promoting inventions, Bacon replaced the ancient suspicion of technological progress with faith in technological progress. The new teaching of collective research, which can make man's lot easier, belong to mankind. Inventions remain with mankind. Men could thus conquer nature, create the universal society and have their utopia. However, only a few men would be really free, because very few are wise.

Allan Bloom pointed out, in his 1987 best seller, *The Closing of the American Mind*, that "If the pursuit of health and safety were to absorb men and they were led to recognize the connection between their preservation and science, the harmony between theory and practice would be established," and the scientists would be the hidden rulers. (p. 287)

A few farsighted Venezuelans realized that Venezuela should have its own laboratories and petroleum research institute, and not depend on the overseas research centres of foreign oil companies. However, first they had to convince others in power and those with the funds to support their effort. Once the need was understood, the struggle began — among those that had the vision and put in the effort to create a petroleum institute in Venezuela.

Over many years of studying the Venezuelan oil industry, I came to understand why nationalization became necessary. Because new concessions were not granted after the last ones in 1957, exploration gradually decreased. In the 1950s, the foreign oil companies averaged drilling a total of about 150 wildcat wells per year. Ten years later, drilling had declined to 40 wildcats per year. With the decline in drilling, Venezuelan oil reserves also declined, as well as personnel in the industry. In 1955, there were about 800 professionals in exploration, but by 1974 there were only 44 professionals.

World demand for products was changing in the 1970s. However, the needed new investments had not been made in upgrading Venezuela's big refineries. Not only was Venezuela not going to be able to market its large exports of residual oil, it was not going to be able to satisfy its domestic market with the growing demand for gasoline. This necessary and expensive upgrading of Venezuela's refining capacity was not going to be made by the majors — not when they knew nationalization was only a matter of time. It was a Catch 22.

Thus, the lack of new concessions spurred nationalization. A country that depended on oil exports for 70% of its foreign exchange, could not avoid doing the latter (nationalize) if it refused to do the former (grant concessions). For sixty years, foreign oil companies had contributed to developing Venezuela.

It was now time to leave! The oil companies were forced to depart; however, the service companies, which represented 45% of the industry's annual costs, did not leave Venezuela and were not nationalized.

With the birth on January 1, 1976, of Petroleos de Venezuela S.A. (PDVSA) and its operating oil affiliates, there was a need for a petroleum research institute. The groundwork had already been laid by Venezuelan scientists, like Marcel Roche and his group in CONICIT in creating Invepet and IVIC's Petroleum and Petrochemical Center, and by oilmen and politicians, all of whom recognized the need for a Venezuelan petroleum research institute. Thus, on the same day that PDVSA came into being, Invepet was presented to the oil industry by the President of Venezuela, Carlos Andres Perez, and he named it Intevep. It, too, would become (in 1979) an affiliate of PDVSA, and this would allow the Instituto

Tecnologico Venezolano del Petroleo (Venezuelan Institute of Petroleum Technology), called Intevep, or the Research & Development Center for Petroleos de Venezuela, to get the needed funding and to grow.

But by going under PDVSA's control, Intevep was organized as a commercial enterprise, as if it was an operator (oil company), instead of a research institute. This is the dilemma: how can a research institute be accepted in "the oil club," and obtain their employee benefits, without having to work under the regulations of a corporation. A research institute needs flexibility, long research lead times on basic research, as well as short term research for more immediate industry needs.

A satisfactory solution to this dilemma is necessary, in order to retain the scientists and researchers, who are essential in producing the technological breakthroughs that the Venezuelan petroleum and petrochemical industry needs. How do oilmen, who are not scientists and researchers, recognize and reward the creative work of these men and women at Intevep? And how does Intevep overcome the Venezuelan trait that what is foreign invented or made is better. This is a handicap that Intevep works under, sometimes even with the affiliates.

In order to study Intevep and its raison d'etre, it is necessary to go back to the beginning of oil research. Laboratories, departments and institutes grew out of a need to better utilize the new discoveries of crude oil in refineries, and to satisfy the growing demand for new products, which changed from kerosene for illumination, to gasoline for transportation, and fuel oil for energy. The development of the internal combustion engine, along with Henry Ford's assembly line, created a growing need for gasoline, and the growing demand for electricity created a need for fuel oil.

It was A. C. Ferris, who found a way, in 1857, to refine crude oil and remove the foul smell. He produced a lamp to burn Seneca oil (kerosene) and displaced whale oil for illumination. Later, with the invention of the incandescent light bulb, electricity displaced kerosene. New uses for crude oil had to be found in the United States, and energy was the logical area. However, long before the U.S. realized the potential of using crude oil for energy, Russia was using fuel oil for the Russian railroads, the metallurgical industry, and in Russian factories.

Downstream — Research in Refining

I n the United States, John D. Rockefeller, in 1868, formally organized the Standard Oil Co. of Pennsylvania, the first to bear the Standard name. Rockefeller wanted to refine a consistent, dependable product that would neither smoke nor explode, and would burn cleanly — a standard oil — batch after batch! At the time, there were 58 refineries in Pittsburgh and 30 in Cleveland, and many more on the East Coast. The composition of a product varied widely from one refiner to another, and from batch to batch. In lighting a lamp, one could not be sure whether it would smoke, or explode! By 1879, Rockefeller controlled 90% of the refining capacity in the United States. He set up the Standard Trust, in 1882, and in 1899 converted it to a holding company — the famous Standard Oil Company of New Jersey!

John Rockefeller and his friends believed the road to dominating the industry was not in producing oil, but in refining and marketing oil. To do this he had to control transportation: first, the railroads, then pipelines, and tankers. Standard Oil (Exxon) was always crude short, and only in Venezuela did Standard become the largest producer. Today, it is a financial institution.

In 1885, Rockefeller created Solar Refining Company, which was a pilot and demonstration refinery to test new technologies to refine Lima, Ohio crudes. In 1887, Herman Frasch, a Canadian chemist who developed a process to refine sour crudes, joined the Solar facilities, and in 1889, the Frasch vapor process became commercial. The Frasch process opened the market for sour crude from Ohio and Canada when it was thought that the production of sweet crude from Pennsylvania and West Virginia had peaked and the U.S. was running out of crude for kerosene. It was the first large scale process to treat high-sulfur crudes. Rockefeller's Standard Oil Trust set up a Manufacturing Committee to evaluate and secure technologies, and once these were acquired, make them available to the companies in the Trust. The Committee also funded research at universities.

William Burton, a Ph.D. from John Hopkins, after working for Frasch in Standard Trust's refining technology, went to work for Standard Oil of Indiana (Amoco). He built their first research facility, near the new Whiting refinery, in 1895. Most of the work at the lab was routine, doing the traditional crude and product testing for the refinery — until 1909, when Burton instructed the lab to work on the problem of increasing the yield of gasoline from crude.

With the development of the automobile, a crude shortage seemed imminent because refinery processes at the time only yielded from 12% to 20% gasoline from crude runs. After the break-up of the Standard Oil Trust by the U.S. Supreme Court, in 1911, Dr. Burton became a Director of Standard of Indiana and he pushed forward a new process in refining that his lab group had been working on, using heat and pressure to crack the residue or bottom fraction and thus convert it into light products, like gasoline. The Burton Process was a milestone for refiners, because they were now able to get a yield of 70% distillates, half of which was gasoline. The Process was patented in 1913, and until 1920, when it became obsolete, it made millions of dollars in profit for Standard Oil of Indiana.

The Burton Process was a turning point in the oil industry, because it invigorated management's thinking about research. Through research they could bring about chemical changes in crude oil. Burton established the need for a new group in the oil industry — researchers, technical innovators who where chemists, engineers and geologists.

The sudden demand for gasoline, in World War I, by the Allied Armies, for their flying machines, spurred the development of new refining processes onward — to the Dubbs Process (by a researcher named Carbon Petroleum Dubbs), which reduced coke deposits. The early refiners depended on heat, i.e., the distillation process, to break crude oil into components or "fractions." Burton and Dubbs added pressure to break down or "crack" the molecule of the gas oil into smaller molecules, such as those of gasoline. These processes collectively became known as "thermal cracking."

It was not just the new demands for products like motor gasoline and aviation fuel that was spurring research in refining processes, it was also the discovery of different crudes, which needed different refining processes to get the desired yield of products. Some of these different crudes were now being imported into the United States, by the companies that made the discoveries abroad; and increasingly they came from Venezuela.

In Europe, imports of Venezuelan crudes also created a need for refining process research. The Venezuelan crudes have high asphaltic content and were different from European crudes, therefore, the Royal Dutch Laboratory in Amsterdam had to solve the problem of refining these new crudes produced by Shell. In 1907, Henri Deterding joined his Royal Dutch Petroleum with the English company, Shell Transport & Trading, to form the Royal Dutch/Shell Group, to better compete against Standard Oil's price cutting in the Far East and Europe. Not only did Royal Dutch/Shell send its Venezuelan crudes to Europe, Standard Oil (after its purchase of Lago in 1932) also sold more Venezuelan crude in Europe.

Royal Dutch/Shell organized two U.S. affiliates in 1912, and the Shell group in the U.S. merged into Shell Oil Company, in 1939. It was Shell that built the first continuous distillation refinery in the U.S., in Martinez, California, in 1915. Shell Development Co. was organized in 1929, to do basic petroleum research in its laboratory at Emeryville, California. The Emeryville lab was started in 1928, as the first laboratory set up by Royal Dutch/Shell that was dedicated to basic research, specifically to find chemical products that could be made from refinery by-product gases. They did not wish this laboratory to become a testing department for a refinery.

Upstream –
Research in Exploration and Development

The oil industry was revolutionized because of Spindletop's discovery, in 1901. Before 1901, Standard Oil stood alone in the United States. After Spindletop, there was a new giant oil producing state - Texas - and it gave birth to new giants in the industry: Gulf Oil, Texaco, Humble, Sun Oil, and Magnolia. And Higgins Oil and Fuel, which was absorbed by Houston Oil Company, became a part of Atlantic-Richfield. In Texas alone, more than 500 oil companies were chartered after Spindletop, and hundreds more from outside the state began operating out of Beaumont, Texas.

A man who was in the center of the eye of this hurricane of change was Pattillo Higgins, of Beaumont. For some nine years he attempted to develop financial interest in Spindletop's oil potential. However, because of — men like John D. Archbold of Standard Oil, who offered to drink every gallon of crude produced west of the Mississippi River, and "professional" geologists like William Kennedy, a Texas state geologist who is credited with delaying the advent of Spindletop by at least six years because of his strongly negative opinions, as well as, Dr. Willard Hayes of the U.S. Geological Survey, who visited the proposed drill sites on

Spindletop and declared no oil would be found because there was no trace of rock strata or oil! — Spindletop's oil and Higgins' salt dome theory were thought to be "loonie."

And ironically and unjustly, when he finally was successful in advertising for an engineer who had knowledge of petroleum and/or sulfur production and found Captain Anthony Lucas, who was able to raise the financial assistance in Pittsburgh, Higgins was locked out by the Mellons. Andrew Mellon and the Mellon Bank agreed to finance an oil venture at Spindletop if Pattillo Higgins were excluded from participation! Therefore, Lucas, John Galley and his partner James M. Guffey, and Gulf Oil are credited with the discovery of Spindletop, but not the man who pushed the dream to realization. Without Pattillo Higgins, the oil industry might have been very different!

While Higgins intuitively knew there was oil in Texas, because of parallels between the topography and geology of the Midwest oil regions and the land around Beaumont, and his intensive self-education, he at first was searching for sources of petroleum in order to fire his kilns to produce better and cheaper bricks in his brick factory. The one-armed Pattillo Higgins found better ways to make bricks, but from bricks he quickly moved on to finding oil fields.

By studying and observing land formations he became a true geologist, as well as an occasional driller, a tool designer, a financier, a landsman, and a legal expert. He discovered that in applying his salt dome theory to petroleum reserves, results were greatly enhanced by drilling on the flanks of the salt dome, instead of on the crest, as he first thought. He had four key indicators that when found in conjunction suggested large pools of subsurface oil to him. He called them nature's own sign. Higgins developed his own surface hydrocarbon geochemical exploration.

Higgins' passion was oil. He was a pioneer in the modern petroleum industry, and became the prototype of the wildcatter. His knowledge of geology and oil production was equal or superior to the "professional" geologists. Between 1905 and 1915, Higgins found more oil fields and had a penchant for starting more companies and had more legal problems than most oilmen ever did in a career. On the 50th anniversary of Spindletop in 1951, and at the age of 88, Higgins claimed to have located over 100 independent oil fields, of which 25 were in production.[2] Higgins' enormous curiosity to know more about the subsurface caused him while drilling at Hockley to drill carefully, extracting core samples at varying levels. This was not being done on a regular basis by other drillers and companies, but it eventually became standard procedure.

Pattillo Higgins planned and developed more efficient tools in his workshop.

From his studies of Herman Frasch's sulfur mining processes, he developed new processes for mining sulfur and obtained a patent. His patents also included one for a drill, a reamer for oil operations, a hydraulic drill mechanism, a drilling gel, and a rock drill. He even devised and patented a pencil sharpener that would hold the pencil and feed it into the sharpener while the operator turned the crank (a most useful tool for a one-armed inventor). Higgins continued to experiment with making bricks of varying weights compositions and clays, and a spin-off was the Indian Pottery Works of San Antonio, which he established in 1927.[3] Today, such creativity would probably be crushed, under our modern system of committees, bureaucracy and legal restraints.

In his book on his grand-uncle, Patillo Higgins, Robert McDaniel points out that while Higgins never revealed what his four indicators for

[2] Robert W. McDaniel, Pattillo Higgins and the Search for Texas Oil (College Station: Texas A & M University Press, 1989), p. 145

[3] Ibid., pp. 138-139

finding oil were, there was probably a fifth indicator: soil color. "It may have been something that he associated with his brickmaking days; that is, the heated kilns produced colored bricks ranging from yellows to bright reds, but the colors were rarely found in 'natural' clays." [4] The heat generated in the creation of oil caused the earth itself to act as a kiln and discolor the topsoil located over this transformation! Higgins was a predecessor in surface geochemical prospecting, which was first performed in 1929, at the Max Planck Institute in Berlin, and expanded in the Soviet Union by V. A. Sokolov by 1932.

Unfortunately, Pattillo Higgins like many researchers never gained the respect or honor he deserved for his large contributions to the oil industry. As a maverick, one of his longest battles was against "big oil" and the "Wall Street sharks," and he was opposed to shipping oil to foreign countries!!!

While some men in Texas did become millionaires, the real profits went to Eastern banking and investment interests. Gulf Oil Corporation (the Mellons) was formed in January 1907, out of the combined assets of two (Mellon) companies: J. M. Guffey Petroleum Co. (Spindletop) and its refining arm, Gulf Refining Company. Gulf and the other companies were to make their profits in Venezuela, after their entrance in the 1920s, and thus became international majors.

After the Spindletop discovery, the price of oil dropped from $2.50/barrel, to as low as 2.5 cents per barrel. The reason for the extreme drop was a lack of use for oil. This severe problem of overabundance of oil was soon resolved by the appearance of the internal combustion engine and the horseless carriage — the automobile! Once George B. Selden's (1878) 3-cylinder internal combustion engine, designed to burn one of the hydrocarbon fractions from crude oil, was patented in 1895, automobilism

---

[4] Ibid., pp. 151-152

among the sporting rich commenced. With the introduction of the electric starter in 1912, in the Cadillac model, the potential driving market doubled — for women could now drive! An early problem encountered by motorists were the dreadful U.S. roads and the too heavy carriages that tore up the roads.

And while Selden was working on the combustion engine, Thomas A. Edison was working in his invention factory at Menlo Park, New Jersey, on a commercially viable system of electric lighting. Edison built up the best equipped laboratory in the U.S., with a team of physicists, chemists, and engineers. Electric lighting not only needed power plants run on oil to generate electricity, it generated a host of new industries, which increased the demand for oil.

Spindletop is an example of how inventiveness and technology has occurred in the petroleum industry. In solving major problems that they encountered as they drilled the discovery well at Spindletop, the Hamill brothers devised a way to drill through 60 feet of quicksand without the sides of the hole collapsing. They created an early form of drilling mud, by driving cattle through a pit to churn up the water. The name "drilling mud" stuck, though it no longer is actually mud. The Hamills also developed well casing, by inserting four-inch pipe inside the eight-inch drill pipe to get through the next hazard at 160 feet, when the well hit a formation of gravel and sand. Once the Lucas gusher roared in, they had to find a way to control it, quickly. Prior to the Spindletop discovery well of 100,000 barrels per day, a 50 b/d well was a giant in Texas. The Hamills whipped up the first Christmas tree within a week, using a system of pipes, clamps, casings, valves, screws and old rope to shut off the flow of oil. Inventing as they proceeded into one new frontier after another has been the tradition of pioneer oilmen.

The United States was the largest oil producer for decades. In 1937, total U. S. oil production had reached 19.9 billion barrels, of this Texas had produced 5.1 billion and California 4.8 billion barrels. At the end of the same year, the Soviet Union had produced a total of 3.7 billion barrels, Mexico 1.8 billion barrels, and Venezuela 1.4 billion barrels of oil. No other producing country had produced one billion barrels. Also in 1937, the United States had about 50% of the world's proved oil reserves, and 62.5% of world production (3.5 million b/d out of 5.6 million b/d). Securing energy resources was a major reason that Japan expanded its conquests of territory into Asia, and attacked Pearl Harbor, in 1941, after President Roosevelt refused to rescind a U.S. embargo on oil and scrap metal shipments to Japan, unless the Japanese stopped aggressive actions in China and Southeast Asia.

Obviously, the world oil market has changed enormously since the United States led in oil production, reserves and research. Now, not only is production and reserves much larger outside the U. S., a great deal of research is going on in other countries. Research is taking place in both private and national oil companies, and companies are selling and buying technology, as well as sharing it in joint ventures.

The discovery system in the petroleum industry works in tandem with all six operations of the industry: from the discovery of oil — to producing the oil — to transporting the oil — to refining the oil — and to finding needed markets or uses for oil products. Some of the discoveries occur in the field, and more complex ones occur in laboratories. Since the discovery of a giant oil field and the excitement of bringing in a gusher is a visual event, the oil finders have been the stars in the petroleum industry.

In spite of its importance to the oil industry, research is not recognized as one of the operations of the industry. Less known, and often unknown, have been the scientists in the laboratories who have perfected the ways and means of using crude oil. Without these men and women crude oil has no value! Why, therefore, has the industry been remiss in recognizing and honoring these scientists? Where is there a Nobel Prize in Petroleum Research type of award?

This book was written to highlight an industry research center in Venezuela, and to acknowledge the contributions of scientists and researchers in the petroleum industry. In addition to analyzing the contributions of industry research in our standard of living and growth in population, this book also highlights Venezuela, the country in the Western Hemisphere: with the largest reserves of oil, the second largest reserves of natural gas; and with the largest reserves of extra-heavy oil in the world! With U.S. imports of oil and gas steadily increasing, are U.S. citizens aware of how important Venezuela is to the United States?

Glossary of Terms

CONICIT - Consejo Nacional de Investigaciones Cientificas y Tecnologicas - 1969

CORDIPLAN - Oficina Central de Coordinacion y Planificacion

FONINVES - Fondo destinado a la Investigacion en Materia de Hidrocarburos y Formacion de Personal Tecnico para la Industria de dichas sustancias - 1972

FUNDACITE - Fundaciones Regionales para el Desarrollo de la Ciencia y la Tecnologia

IDEA - Instituto Internacional de Estudios Avanzados

Intevep - Instituto Technologico Venezolano del Petroleo - 1976

Invepet - Fundacion para la Investigacion en Hidrocarburos y Petroquimica - 1974

IVIC - Instituto Venezolano de Investigaciones Cientificas - 1959

IVNIC - Instituto Venezolano de Neurologia e Investigaciones Cerebrales - 1955

PDVSA - Petroleos de Venezuela, S.A. - 1976

CHAPTER I

RESEARCH: THE SPRINGBOARD TO MODERN TECHNOLOGY

N ature created petroleum, which was of little use until man gave petroleum value by refining it into kerosene to light his lamps, and into fuel oil to run his trains, ships and factories. By processing or refining crude oil into useful products, man found a way to utilize this mineral resource. The use of petroleum goes back to Biblical times and the beginnings of recorded history. It was used as pitch for water-proofing cloth and boats, for lighting and heating, for medicine, and for war as flame throwers.

However, before oil can be processed it must be found in sufficiently large volumes - and produced! *Upstream operations* commence with the geologist who searches for petroleum by surveying geological structures. The next operation is to drill for petroleum, and when oil is discovered it must then be developed and produced. In the *downstream operations*, oil must be transported, then refined, and finally marketed to customers.

While the upstream operations of the oil industry are complicated, most industry laboratories were initially built to do research on developing better products downstream, i.e., on processing petroleum: crude oil, natural gas or asphalt, into useful products, or on improving the engines or end-receiver of these products.

Laboratories were first set up near refineries to help them adapt to differences in crude characteristics from different regions. Later, the laboratories were enlarged or new ones were built to confront two important technological events: the invention of electric light, and the internal combustion engine! These external events forced the oil industry to undertake new process research to respond to the decline in demand for kerosene, and the steady growth in gasoline demand.

Currently, most people who happen to write on the history of research in the petroleum industry give credit to Standard Oil and the Royal Dutch/Shell Group, as the most important companies in the creation of research laboratories and for breakthroughs in oil industry research. The focus of these articles is on post World War I and World War II industry funded research at company research and development centers. However, before the twentieth century when these large oil companies started setting up their research centers, the Nobel brothers of Russia had set up the first major research facilities and made great breakthroughs.

For these many accomplishments in Russia, one man stands out as a giant: Ludwig Nobel, son of, Immanuel Nobel of Sweden who immigrated to St. Petersburg, Russia, in 1838. There were Nobels in Russia for the next 80 years. Immanuel's sons, Robert and Ludwig, entered the oil industry in Baku.

The Russian Nobels

The Nobel laboratory in St. Petersburg, Russia was established by Ludwig Nobel around 1880. Its primary purpose was to find varied and efficient uses for Nobel Brothers' (Branobel, known as Nobel) petroleum. One of Ludwig's concerns was with the development of natural-draft fuel oil burners. He was searching for a means by which the burners would leave no residue and produce no smoke. Ludwig's goal was to have the Russian navy use oil burners throughout the fleet, not just on the Caspian Sea. However, the navy was not convinced - not until 20 years later. No other major power was converting to oil, so the Russians did not want to take the chance.

Ludwig Nobel's contributions to research were many, and some of these were accomplished outside the laboratory. Just as the engineer in the oil industry solves technical problems in both the upstream and downstream operations, thereby inventing/ discovering new means and products, so did the Swedish Nobel in Russia.

It should be mentioned that it was Ludwig's brother, Alfred Nobel, who was the first to combine successfully his invention (of dynamite) with business organization and financial management, opening a new era in 1864. And it was the "premature news" of his death in 1888, when his brother Ludwig died at Cannes on the Riviera, at age 57, that caused Alfred to rewrite his will leaving all his fortune to purposes that no obituary would ever condemn, as well as, guarantee his fame forever! When Ludwig died, some of the press in Europe got the brothers mixed up and reported that Alfred Nobel had died. Alfred had the displeasure of reading obituaries condemning the munitions maker "who had made so much money finding new ways to maim and kill."[1] Alfred died in December 1896, and has since been remembered for the Nobel Foundation, and the annual coveted prizes - the Nobel Prize in Peace, Economics, Medicine, Literature, etc.. Ironically, his brother Ludwig, who created the Russian petroleum industry, was forgotten!

After Robert Nobel purchased the first parcels of oil land in Baku along with a small refinery in 1873, he set about improving methods of refining the crude oil, to produce a higher-grade kerosene than that produced by the other Baku refineries. Robert was a good chemist, and his modernized refinery produced the highest-quality kerosene in Russia. The Nobel refinery could compete in quality with the US-American kerosene, which dominated the Russian market. Nobel kerosene first arrived in St. Petersburg in October 1876, and marked the beginning of the end for U.S. distributors in Russia. By 1883, the US-Americans were shut out of the Russian market.

---

[1] Robert W. Tolf, *The Russian Rockefellers,* (Stanford, Calif.: Hoover Institution Press, 1976), p.109

When Ludwig Nobel entered Baku in 1876, he was impressed with what Robert had achieved, but he also realized the tremendous potential. Ludwig began to research and discuss with engineers and other technicians specific ways to improve efficiency and expand Robert's operations.

He separated the studies into four main categories of pipelines, pumps, rail transport, and storage; he summarized all information currently available to him and then listed a series of questions that had to be answered before further consideration could be given to adoption of new practices in Baku.[2]

Ludwig laid the first oil pipeline in Baku, in 1877, which took only a year to be paid in full. Next, he devised a better way than wooden barrels and sailing ships to ship kerosene *and* residual oil from Baku. Ludwig devised a way to transport crude oil and oil products in bulk, by building the first oil tanker. The tanker was one of the most important contributions in the history of the oil industry. It was a discovery that would rank with Alfred's invention of dynamite. Ludwig proved that the skin of the vessel could be used as the outer shell of the oil container.

Ludwig Nobel was a walking research laboratory! He drew his tanker, built exclusively for bulk transport of oil. His education in marine engineering, earned on the Navy's steam engines, enabled him to surmount safety considerations: "sealing off the oil from the boiler area, making allowances for expansion and contraction caused by temperature changes, ventilating the hold so no gases could accumulate."[3] He had the world's first tanker, the *Zoroaster*, built in Sweden, in 1878. It was also one of the first ships in the world to use Bessemer steel. The Nobel factory in St. Petersburg designed and built pumps and other special equipment, and Ludwig designed the series of 21 vertical watertight compartments, which were essential to keep the ship afloat during rough weather. The Caspian Sea, where the *Zoroaster* and her sister ships would sail, was as dangerous to sail as any ocean. The engine amidship and the cisterns in the hold joined by pipes proved to be seaworthy, and revolutionary. The *Zoroaster* was studied, "copied by shipping firms and brokers, draftsmen and designers, oil industrialists and government officials."[4] The tanker was open to

---

[2] Ibid., p. 51
[3] Ibid., p. 55
[4] Ibid.

inspection and imitation, for Ludwig rejected the pleas of his associates that he take out patents.

Ludwig continued improving his designs, and in 1880, he ordered a new type of tanker that utilized the shell as the wall of the bulk cargo hold. In this tanker, the kerosene completely filled the storage area from side to side and up to the deck. Partitioned sections fore and aft provided buoyancy and served as the crew's quarters and pump room. The first of these tankers was christened *Moses* (others were named *Mohammed*, *Spinoza*, *Socrates*, *Darwin*, *Koran*, and *Talmud*).

As always, the usual critics of those who invent or dare to improve the lot of man appeared when transport accidents occurred, and the voices of alarm joined the chorus of opponents to Ludwig's innovations. However, adversity only spurred Ludwig to invent further. He discovered that when loading oil, what was needed was a flexible pipe, a leakproof conduit with couplings that could move with the ship and remain firmly fastened to the tanker's loading hole.[5] Ludwig's new pipe became standard equipment on tankers, and was replaced years later by the steel-coil reenforced rubber hoses.

Despite their knowledge of the *Zoroaster*, the US-Americans and the British were reluctant to risk building overseas tankers. It was a German, Heinrich Riedemann of Bremen, who built the *Andromede*, which was the first tanker to cross the Atlantic with a cargo of oil, in 1884. However, Riedemann's *Gluckauf*, built in Newcastle, was the first real tanker to cross the ocean, in 1885. When the *Gluckauf* arrived in New York to take on its first cargo of oil, the barrel industry threatened so strongly, that the tanker departed without loading any oil. It was not until the following year that a load of bulk oil was dispatched in Geestemunde that a milestone was reached.[6] It took eight years, after Ludwig Nobel had given the world a working model of a tanker, for it to be accepted and copied outside of Russia - and the worldwide revolution in transportation to get underway.

The research accomplishments of Ludwig Nobel boggle the mind. There has been no one else like him in the petroleum industry. He not only conceived of pipelines, and the first tanker, he created in 10 years an entire oil empire, inventing as he went. He designed tank barges for transshipment, gigantic storage tanks and reservoirs, railroad tankcars and

---

[5]   Ibid., p. 57
[6]   Ibid., p. 59

barges to carry the Nobel oil to all corners of Russia. Ludwig organized sales areas, arranged bank loans, and oversaw company finances. "He was president, chief engineer, sales manager, an entire research and development department, chairman of the board, and market analyst."[7]

Ludwig Nobel always acted in a generous manner once he thought of a new invention. He would contact the other major producers in Baku with his idea, and after each negative response he would then proceed alone. Along with all of his oil operations he built a huge company railroad, with 1500 tank cars and dozens of locomotives, in order to distribute petroleum products during the long winter when the Volga River was frozen and river transportation halted. He also built huge distribution depots to store his oil. By 1900, there were 129 Nobel depots in Russia.

Besides the oil tanker, the other great research contribution to the oil industry that Ludwig made was a new refining system based on continuous distillation. In 1881, Ludwig and Alfred Tornquist (whom he'd sent to the United States to learn all he could about the refining processes) installed the first multi-still continuous refining system ever adapted for commercial use, in Baku. The battery of stills was arranged so that each successive still with its higher temperature was placed lower than the preceding one, so that the oil flowed by gravity continuously through the entire series of stills. "Distillates from the various stills reached the tailhouse separately but they were all combined into one of three products: kerosene, gasoline, and the distillate from the air condenser which was called black kerosene."[8] This was redistilled as was the low gravity gasoline.

The new system Ludwig devised produced the highest quality kerosene. Samples were constantly checked to ensure uniform quality. Ludwig's system yielded 35% kerosene from the crude, nearly double what other refiners produced, and there were no interruptions in the refining process for repair and the periodic draining and cleaning of stills. One or two stills if taken out of use did not shut down the whole process. Ludwig used sulfuric acid as a kerosene purifier, discovered by the German chemist, Herman Frasch, in the United States. The Nobels also used caustic soda as a cleaning agent in the post refining quality control.

[7]   Ibid., p. 61
[8]   Ibid., pp. 67-68

The refining system of continuous distillation was not used in the United States, until 34 years later, by Shell Oil in their Martinez, California refinery.

The laboratories that Ludwig established were used to do research on ways and means of increasing the yield, and purifying their products. While Ludwig lived, the Nobel laboratory in Petersburg worked mainly on kerosene, lubricants and fuel oil. He studied the feasibility of refining gasoline, useful then in the manufacture of rubber. The Nobels had the first gasoline refinery in Russia, several years prior to World War I. In the 1880s, however, it was fuel oil consumption in Russia, initially by the railroads, then with industrialization in the metallurgical industries and factories in the north, that was more important than the consumption of kerosene! Russia was industrializing. As usual, Ludwig made his contributions, with improved new oil burners: stationary boilers, locomotive and ship boilers.

Ludwig Nobel believed in no secrets, no monopolies, and no special privileges. The Nobel enterprises that Ludwig ran had a higher discipline and loyalty than others in Russia because of Ludwig's concern for his workers' welfare. He insisted "on improving the lot of the worker, on providing decent housing, a living wage, safe and secure conditions, recreational facilities, and opportunities for self-improvement."[9] Ludwig introduced a profit-sharing plan, provided improved housing, offered free education, established technical schools, and ordered construction of the famous oil community, Villa Petrolea. This was a walled in camp of homes and apartments for the executives of Branobel in Baku. Some have said that Ludwig's Petrolea was as great a contribution to later generations, as the tankers, refineries, distribution network and all of the innovations that sprang forth from this incredible man.

A footnote should be added about the Russian Nobels who have been forgotten by the world, but who contributed so very much to the oil industry. The Smithsonian Institution in its petroleum exhibit in the 1960s identified Riedemann's *Gluckauf* as the "first tanker." And Exxon Corporation in a television commercial in 1973, also claimed that the *Gluckauf* was "the first vessel built expressly as an oil tanker."[10] If the Russian Revolution of 1917 had not occurred, perhaps the Nobel brothers

---

[9]   Ibid., p. 72
[10]   Ibid., p.238

and their great contributions would not have been forgotten. We would instead know that the first laboratory in the oil industry was built by Ludwig Nobel, as was the first tanker, the first modern refinery, the first quality control system, and the first well designed oil camp!

We Begin with the Chemist

The chemical industry, which has been so closely tied to the petroleum industry, had its beginning in 1856, with the discovery of synthetic purple dye by a 17-year old chemistry student, William Henry Perkin, who was studying at the Royal College of Chemistry in England. Before his discovery, the most highly prized dye was purple, because it was obtained from the gland of certain shellfish, and therefore, was very costly. Purple dye had been limited in its use to the robes of kings and queens. Perkin, while trying to synthesize quinine from coal tar, a byproduct of the iron industry, noted that this black product, when boiled with water, gave a purple solution. He found that this mauve dye would adhere to silk. By the end of 1857, Perkin had built a chemical plant to manufacture this most prized dye. The name "coal-tar dyes" was applied to the new dyes developed in rapid succession by Perkin. Mr. Perkin retired at the age of 35 as a wealthy man, however, he continued his research as a chemist in the field of organic chemistry until he died, in 1907.

Thus, color helped to establish chemistry as a science and an industry. This also was the beginning of industries and universities working together, and it commenced in Germany. German chemists in the nineteenth century, were quick to see the potential of this union. From these new efforts grew the dye industry, explosives industry, pharmaceutical industry, and fertilizer industry. And in the twentieth century, the petrochemical industry was to change man's living standard even more than the previous contributions through chemistry.

Chemistry is concerned with the transformation of matter, i.e., how various chemical changes can occur, and the causes and effects of these changes. Geology is allied with chemistry, in its fundamental concern with the earth's composition. As each science looks at matter, they discover that all the scientific distinctions of separate studies merge into a common need for understanding molecular and atomic particles. However, it is because matter has become so complex that we must start where we are, and then find methods to unravel the more complex forms, so that we can discover what are the simplest basic units.

The Ancient Greeks were our teachers. Plato showed us in his *Republic* that knowledge is not pursued for the sake of knowledge by "the intellectual," because to the extent to which a man is devoted to his calling, he forgets his own advantage. Only the things of the mind can belong to all men. Thus, Socrates' view of philosophy was that knowledge is the highest good! Love of learning for the philosopher is his longing for completeness. He wants to know everything, aware that no part can be understood without being considered in relation to the whole. And yet, wisdom is knowledge of ignorance! There is no knowledge of the whole, only knowledge of parts. Because of the elusiveness of the whole, a return to the beginning remains a constant necessity.

Socrates and Plato showed us in the Greek dialogues how man acquires knowledge by starting at the beginning, just as a child who learns to read begins with the letters of the alphabet, or a man looks in a pool and sees the reflection of a tree in it, then leans over and sees himself for the first time! Socrates started by asking questions: What is man? What is the soul? What is justice? What is wisdom?

In science, man must proceed from the known to the unknown. He, thus, can begin to discover how the basic units have come together to form the complex world in which we live. The scientist's task is to undertake methods of classification of all forms of matter so that its complexity may be understood. It is the chemist who ultimately reduces the matter he studies to a molecular and atomic level. He assigns a molecular formula and structure to each bit of matter that has been isolated from all other bits of matter. Through the chemist's efforts we have learned to isolate pure substances from mixtures.

Modern science in the beginning evolved slowly. Beginning with Thomas Aquinas's *Summa Theologica*, in the thirteenth century, science was still restrained by theological dogma. Slowly a gradual scientific revolution began under men like Copernicus (1473-1543), Kepler (1571-1630) and Galileo (1564-1642), Robert Boyle (1620-1691), and Sir Isaac Newton (1642-1727). Boyle and Newton began to reassert the concept of the atomic theory and urge the break from the four-element theory. Over time, the scientist discovered that matter consisted of 103-odd elements, which we now consider the basic building blocks of the universe.

Sulfur

The use of sulfur goes back as far as recorded history. The Egyptians burned sulfur to banish evil spirits, and they dyed their fabrics in its smoke. In Greece, Homer referred to its use as a disinfectant. And the Chinese, around 500 B.C., began using small quantities of sulfur in the manufacture of gunpowder. Alchemists, in the Middle Ages, experimented with the pale-yellow mineral, hoping to turn it into gold. Their experiments led to the discovery of sulfuric acid, which is today's most widely used chemical. Referred to as the ninth most abundant element in the universe, sulfur is commonly found in small amounts in crude oil, natural gas and coal. It was even found in the rocks brought back from the Moon, by the Apollo astronauts. Sulfur is a most important element, for it enables plants and animals to synthesize proteins. Humans need sulfur for our metabolism. And it is the fourth major plant nutrient after nitrogen, phosphorus and potassium.

In an article on sulfur, in Exxon's *The Lamp*, Fall 1990, Denise Allen Zwicher states that sulfur is so important, it "is considered a major indicator of a country's standard of living." It has been used in medicines to treat many diseases like tuberculosis, pneumonia, high blood pressure, and rheumatism. Around 90% of the world's sulfur is used to produce sulfuric acid, a raw material used in many chemical processes. Along with salt, limestone, coal and oil, sulfur is considered one of the five basic raw materials of the chemical industry.

Up to 1903, Sicily supplied 85% of the world's supply from shaft mines. Oil drillers in Louisiana and Texas discovered another major source of sulfur - deposits deep underground, usually found with salt domes. The sulfur could not be mined conventionally, but Herman Frasch, once more came to the rescue, and the German chemical engineer invented a process for recovering the sulfur by melting it underground with superheated steam. The Frasch process was the leading method for sulfur recovery for 50 years, from 1900 to the mid-1950s.

In the 1960s, the major source of sulfur changed, again. With increased demand for petroleum, oil companies were forced to produce oil fields that contained an excessive amount of sulfur. At the same time, sulfur removal from oil production became essential because of environmental and economic reasons. The environmental reasons were due to 1) sulfur dioxide, a result of when sulfur and certain sulfur compounds burn and combine with oxygen; and 2) acid rain, a result of sulfur dioxide combining with water in the upper atmosphere and forming dilute sulfurous acid. The economic reasons are the highly corrosive sulfur compounds effect on metals used in pipelines and refineries. Sulfur recovery from crude oil and natural gas now accounts for more than 40% of the world's sulfur production. Mined sulfur decreased, as sulfur recovery by the petroleum industry increased.

Sulfur removal begins at the wellhead, by contacting natural gas with a solvent that absorbs hydrogen sulfide gas from the gas stream, which is then stripped out of the solvent and sent to a sulfur-recovery unit. Crude oil is stripped of hydrogen sulfide as it comes out of the well. The more complex sulfur molecules are removed at the refinery. Most modern refineries and gas plants use different forms of the Claus process, a sulfur-recovery process developed in 1883, by C. F. Claus, a British chemical engineer.

The degree of processing required depends on the level of sulfur in the crude, however, any additional processing increases the costs of the products. Fortunately, there is a growing demand for sulfur, and some of the costs can be recovered through the sale of sulfur by the oil industry - generally through their chemical companies. This growing demand for sulfur is opportune, because oil companies are drilling deeper into reservoirs with higher temperatures and pressures, increasing the probability they will encounter sour gas and oil. (Crude oil and gas containing sulfur compounds are considered sour.)

Chemical Engineers

In an article by Ralph Landau and Nathan Rosenberg in *Invention & Technology* magazine, Fall 1990 issue, the authors state that "Chemicals is the industry that spends the most non-government money on research and development — more than $11 billion a year," — and the industry spends more on basic research than any other industry. They also point out that it is one of only two (the other is aerospace) that maintains a positive balance of payments in international trade. It was the World War I cutoff of organic chemical imports from Germany that forced the U.S. to develop its own chemical supplies. The

U.S. thus pioneered the worldwide conversion of the organic-chemicals industry from a coal to a petroleum base. "It is the *chemical engineering* profession that equipped the nation's industry to make the most of these opportunities."[11]

The chemical industry is crucial in the provision of our food, clothing, shelter, and health. It is vital in the petroleum, rubber, steel-making, aluminum, and paper industries. It is "a locus of creative activity that has spilled over into a host of other endeavors."[12]   Between 1899-1946, the chemical industry in the U.S. accounted for more than a quarter of all new industrial - laboratory foundings. First, the scientific experiment occurs at the laboratory, and then the chemical engineer translates small-scale reactions to full industrial manufacturing processes.

Landau and Rosenberg point out that the skills needed to design and coordinate chemical-processing equipment involves an educational curriculum very different from that of a chemist or a mechanical engineer. The discipline of the chemical engineer mainly evolved at Massachusetts Institute of Technology. This was in sharp contrast to Germany where in the nineteenth century the chemists generally handed over their findings to mechanical engineers, and the two professions maintained separate roles. At first, this was the case in the United States, but this began to change at MIT under William H. Walker, a chemistry professor and his colleague, the famous chemical consultant, Arthur D. Little. Dr. Walker's reorganization of courses in chemistry and mechanical engineering into a unified program, evolved into the study of unit operations, which was a concept espoused by Arthur D. Little, in 1915. Under unit operations, the vast number of industrial chemical processes were reduced to a few basic steps: distillation, absorption, heat transfer, and filtration, etc. An engineer trained in unit operations could mix and match a wide range of individual products and processes.

In 1916, Dr. Walker and a younger colleague, Warren K. Lewis, founded the School of Chemical Engineering Practice, with Little's support. In the 1920s, the chemical engineering program grew rapidly. Dr. Lewis developed a relation with the oil refining industry, particularly with

---

[11] Ralph Landau and Nathan Rosenberg,"America's High-Tech Triumph," in *American Heritage of Invention & Technology*, (New York: American Heritage, a division of Forbes Inc., Fall 1990), Vol. 6, no. 2, p. 59
[12] Ibid., p. 58

Standard Jersey. He helped increase oil recovery by introducing the use of vacuum stills, thus avoiding coking and fouling up the cracking furnaces, by operating at lower temperatures. Lewis's vacuum stills became standards in refineries and raised the average yield of gasoline from 18% to 36% of crude.

On the advise of Dr. Lewis, Standard Jersey in 1927, located a new research staff composed of Dr. Robert T. Haslam from MIT and a group of 13 other young staffers and graduates of MIT, at the Jersey refinery at Baton Rouge, Louisiana, on the Mississippi River. Dr. Haslam was professor of chemical engineering and director of the Institute's School of Chemical Engineering Practice and of the its Research Laboratory of Applied Chemistry, however, his appointment to Jersey became permanent. The Baton Rouge site was chosen because of the plentiful supply of natural gas and crude oil in the vicinity of the refinery. The new research group was to work principally on hydrogeneration — adapting the coal hydrogeneration process, developed by I. G. Farben to petroleum operations. In 1927, Standard Jersey signed a 25-year contract with I. G. Farben, a combination of German companies organized in 1926, which was the most advanced in the world in the chemical research industry.[13] In the 1920s, Germany was the world's leader in industrial research and U.S. companies turned to their German counterparts for assistance in research.

The results of this combination — of MIT chemical engineers, the new Baton Rouge laboratories, and the association with a leading German research group — paid off handsomely for Standard Jersey. "Many of the most important new developments in petroleum processing before World War II originated at this Baton Rouge center, where pilot plants of appropriate sizes could be built and technically supported."[14] The Baton Rouge laboratories introduced: hydroforming, fluid flex coking, and fluid catalytic cracking, which became the most important source of propylene and butane.

Dr. Lewis had focused the discipline of chemical engineering on an overall systems approach to the design of continuous automated processing, first in petroleum refining and later in chemicals.[15]

[13] Larson, Knowlton, Popple, *New Horizons 1927-1950*, History of Standard Oil Company (New Jersey), (New York: Harper & Row, 1971), p. 153.
[14] "America's High-Tech Triumph," p. 60
[15] Ibid., p. 61

The petrochemical industry, which followed, benefited from the research on continuous processing in petroleum refining. The new petrochemical industry was started in the United States, shortly before World War II, by a few companies: Union Carbide, Shell, Dow, and Standard Jersey.

After the War, the U.S. chemical engineering field developed with great speed, allowing the U.S. petrochemical industry to help improve the U.S. standard of living and contribute to raising the world's standard of living. The U.S. chemical industry emerged not only unscathed from World War II, but strengthened by wartime crash programs. The European chemical industry was damaged and after the War was rebuilt separately in each country, therefore, because of limited national markets they did not scale up as U.S. companies did.

With the rapid growth of this U.S. industry, new specialized engineering firms that could design and engineer chemical production processes multiplied. A few of these firms had appeared earlier, catering to petroleum refining, e.g., Universal Oil Products (UOP) and M.W. Kellogg Company. Production costs would go down only when the scale of each reaction system was increased by using a single "train," or chemical assembly line. The new engineering firms often did the whole job of developing manufacturing installations for major chemical companies. These specialized firms attracted talented chemists and chemical engineers by giving them more freedom and even a financial stake in the firm.

U. S. firms after World War II dominated the world chemical market, and worked hard to develop new chemical technologies, which were rapidly dispersed worldwide. The specialized engineering firms, along with the new licensing arrangements between companies, contributed to dispersing this new technology. Most important, with this competition costs for chemical products fell, leading to lower prices and more accessible chemical technology!

Petroleum Engineers

The petroleum engineers were making important contributions to producing technology, solving problems as they drilled deeper wells. They devised ways of reducing the number of blowouts, of drilling through heaving shales, improving the cementing of deep wells, and designed faster drilling bits. They raised the efficiency of all aspects of producing operations.

The engineer is needed at every stage of oil operations. Engineering skills are needed to produce crude oil and natural gas, to manufacture, to store, to transport and to distribute its many products. The changing conditions, under which the engineer works in the search for and the production of petroleum, maximizes their effort, which is the foundation upon which all other petroleum activities rest. It can be said that the engineer invents as he solves problems. The oil field is his laboratory! The petroleum engineer is called upon to improvise. Petroleum engineers are in a contest with nature to provide the products to meet human needs. It is a hunt that never ends.

The petroleum engineer starts to drill test wells once the geologist or geophysicist decides on the probability that oil is in a particular location. The drilling of test wells is the most costly single operation in oil exploration. The rotary drilling method is the one most often used. Extensive oil accumulation is discovered by drilling a number of wells carefully spaced near the discovery well. The lifting of oil to the ground surface and the handling of oil above ground will depend a great deal on the nature of the oil and its associated gas. Crude oil can range from very heavy viscous with little or no gas dissolved in it and under very low pressure, up to an extremely light oil with a high volume of gas, known as a condensate-type crude. The latter are more likely to be found at great depths. After drilling and examining oil samples, which show their characteristics and physical attributes, and determining the oil reservoir is large enough to be commercial, the petroleum engineer must determine how many wells should be drilled in the reservoir.

Proven reserves can tie up large sums of capital, therefore, the oil company usually desires maximum efficient rates (MER) wherever possible. In most reservoirs, natural energy drive is available to move the oil in the reservoir to the well bore, because the oil is trapped under conditions of relative high pressures and temperatures. There are five natural energy sources: 1) reservoir compaction and fluid expansion, 2) free gas cap, 3) solution gas, 4) water drive, and 5) gravity drive. These energy sources may act independently or in combination in any particular reservoir. Reservoir engineers must determine porosity, permeability, and the amount of oil and water in the pore space. The type of recovery mechanism to use depends on these and other factors, and on latter evidence collected after production commences.

One of the engineer's most important jobs is determining the oil reserves of a field. There are three basic methods of determining oil reserves: 1) volumetric calculation, 2) material balance reserve estimate, and 3) decline curve reserve estimate. Usually, the higher the production peak, the sooner the decline curve can be expected to begin and the steeper that decline curve may be.

Royal Dutch/Shell Group

The Royal Dutch/Shell Group of Companies was formed by merging the interests of Royal Dutch (60%) and Shell Transport (40%), in 1907. More than any other oil company, the Shell Group has emphasized research. The first central laboratory was set up in October 1895, at Delft in Holland. Its primary responsibility was to develop and apply methods of analyzing and inspecting petroleum products. As with most of the oil companies, Shell also set up quality control laboratories wherever they were needed. In 1902, the Royal Dutch Company opened a control laboratory for its Charlois (Rotterdam) gasoline redistilling plant. In 1914, the large Amsterdam laboratory opened.

After first exporting gasoline from Sumatra to the U.S. West Coast, in 1912, Shell formed the Roxana Petroleum Company in Oklahoma, in October. The following year, Shell purchased California Oilfields, Ltd., in Coalinga, California. In 1915, they built a new refinery in Martinez, California, which was *the U.S.'s first continuous process refinery*. And then in 1921, Shell had their first major strike in the United States - the famous Signal Hill, California field, near Long Beach. With this oil production, Shell built two new refineries, one at Wilmington (1923), and another at Dominguez (1927). A Shell holding company was formed in Delaware in 1922, with Royal Dutch Shell Group holding 65%. This publicly held corporation existed until 1985, when it became a 100% Group owned company.

Initial research by Shell in the United States, began in 1916. A year after the Martinez refinery was completed, a lab was set up on the grounds. And in 1922, a separate building to house investigational work was built. Their first project was the removal of sulfur and gum from distillates.

Shell's commitment to research was assured after Shell Development Company was organized in 1928. Its first laboratory was built at Emeryville, California, to do basic petroleum research - to find chemical products that could be made from refinery byproduct gases. And a year later, Shell Chemical was formed to manufacture these products. "Disapproval of waste in any form, a thoroughly Dutch characteristic, had led to the creation ... of these two Shell companies ...."[16] There was a great deal of waste gas not only in the oilfields, but in refineries as well, which was either flared, or burned for boiler fuel. Shell attacked this problem earlier than other companies. And the Shell Group was the first oil company to enter and succeed in the chemical business. (Standard of Jersey did attempt to manufacture isopropyl alcohol from petroleum in 1920, but like other oil companies then, it lacked the needed research background.)

The Dutchmen in Holland realized that the men operating the refineries were too close to the problem. The refiners had their hands full developing and perfecting cracking processes and in obtaining maximum gasoline yields, to have time to worry about waste gases. It was the younger J. B. Aug. Kessler, who had an intense interest in the scientific aspects of the oil business. His election in 1924, as a Royal Dutch managing director was an important milestone in the history of the Group's research activity.[17]

The first step was to apply known chemistry to develop laboratory reactions into full-scale commercial processes, to produce saleable products. Thus, the Shell Group entered the chemical business via the manufacture of synthetic ammonia. On Shell Point, near Pittsburg, California, they built the first synthetic ammonia plant to use natural gas (instead of coke oven gas), to obtain hydrogen. Shell Point's ammonia plant cost $5 million to build, and started up in August 1931. However, that was not a good year to start a new business, during the Depression and one year before the Crash. "In its first five years, Shell Chemical cost its backers a net of $6,231,000 in deficit, loans, and stock subscriptions."[18] The Shell Group realized that the commitment would be costly and that it would take time before they might realize a profit.

---

[16] Kendall Beaton, *Enterprise in Oil*, A History of Shell In the United States (New York: Appleton-Century-Crofts, Inc., 1957), p. 502

[17] Ibid., p. 503

[18] Ibid., p. 524

Shell's innovative California ammonia plant had a number of break-throughs: they developed a means of using acid sludge from the refineries to make ammonium sulphate; they increased output by the introduction of "double operation" by using their stand-by equipment as a second plant; marketing a byproduct, pure carbon, for use in the metallurgy industry; and developing a new method of applying ammonia fertilizers to land under cultivation. The latter, a system of metering liquid ammonia from pressure cylinders directly into California irrigation ditches, was called "Nitrogation."

The Shell Group had to acquire scientific knowledge in the field of organic chemistry. (Inorganic chemistry had evolved from the alchemy of the Middle Ages.) The substances in greatest demand by industry, i.e., leather, textiles, dyes, etc., were organic, of animal or vegetable origin. However, these organic materials were far less simple than ordinary inorganic chemistry. A present ingredient in all of these complicated and useful organic substances was carbon.

In the mid-Nineteenth Century, the molecular theory of matter and the theory of linkages offered the first plausible explanation of isomerism. Molecular theory explained the smallest particles of a given substance were molecules, and they in turn consisted of atoms of the various chemical elements. However, what held them together? Perhaps the atoms of some elements had more invisible bonds (arms): thus the theory of linkages evolved, along with the structural formulae, which we now use to express this relationship. This was the key to a whole new science - the chemistry of carbon compounds known as organic chemistry. And eventually, it became the key to a whole new industry, an oil based chemical industry.

Shell was the first to jump in! First, in the Amsterdam laboratory, in the mid-1920s, Shell began gas research. However, Amsterdam was not the best place for cracking-gas research, as it was far away from cracking installations. It was decided in The Hague that Shell would establish a separate research center in the United States. But first, a careful study was made of *where* the laboratory would be built, and *how* it would be set up!

The research laboratory would be set up in such a manner that it could not degenerate into a testing department for a refinery. It would be separate from the existing Shell Companies in the United States. It would employ the best academic scientists it could find, put them under competent direction, and leave them alone to work in an atmosphere of complete freedom! It would need to be near a good university so that its staff could use the scientific library and have daily contact with fellow scientists in the academic world. It must be located near a source of natural gas, and be near enough to a refinery to receive supplies of cracked gases and other materials. Finally, the lab should be near enough to one of the company's main offices to take advantage of its administrative facilities.

These wise Dutchmen realized that a certain distance with a certain proximity had to be balanced properly, along with a strong dose of freedom, to guarantee successful results. They were obviously concerned lest a supervisory bureaucracy saddle and hamstring their researchers, and they prevented this from happening by the last specification. This laboratory would not be run like an oil company!

The choice was Emeryville, a small industrial community directly opposite San Francisco, on the Bay, adjoining Berkeley and the University of California. The Martinez refinery was near enough, and Shell's California head office was in San Francisco. The Emeryville laboratory was built and equipped in just four months and total cost was $200,000. The research director, who designed and oversaw the project, Dr. E. Clifford Williams, an Englishman, moved in with his small staff, in October 1928. By 1939, the number employed at Emeryville had grown to over 500.

The Emeryville laboratory researched chemicals that could be made from refinery waste gases. They concentrated on propylene and the butylenes for the next 10 years. Soon, Emeryville had a pilot plant making secondary butyl alcohol. In his book, *Enterprise in Oil*, History of Shell in the United States, Kendall Beaton points out that Shell's development of continuous processing techniques in the new petroleum chemical industry was to differ from the coal-tar chemical business, and thus, made possible cheaper chemicals than otherwise would have been the case. (p. 532) The next order of business was the sale of these new chemicals, the majority of which were new products. Therefore, in 1932, Shell Development Company formed a market development department.

The next phase of basic research at Emeryville was oil-refining technology, followed by physical research, oil-production research, and research on the application of chemical products. This meant additional staff, acreage and building construction, by 1938. And now a new, very important project was started: *substitutive chlorination*. "This unorthodox chemical reaction was to open up a whole new field of industrial chemicals, the allyl derivatives, which up to now had been in the realm of laboratory chemicals."[19]   Between 1936 and 1948, Shell Chemical was to make the bulk of its new plant expenditures around substitutive chlorination and their derived processes. "The publication of the process in detail in 1940 constitutes one of Shell Development's outstanding contributions to scientific knowledge."[20]

It should be noted here that Shell's contributions to scientific knowledge emerged from their global perspective. Prior to World War II, the United States was very weak in basic research. Most basic research was done in Europe, mainly in Germany, and prior to World War I in Russia, by the Nobels and others. Shell researchers' multilingual abilities, plus their European background, drew their attention to the work of European scientists.

In the case of substitutive chlorination, Shell Development made a thorough study of the reactions of hydrocarbons with chlorine. The results were startling. A synthetic glycerine process was started, in 1936. Shell Development was already producing methallyl chloride from substitutive chlorination.   By 1937, the *synthetic glycerine process* had gone through pilot-plant operation, and at the API Meeting in Chicago, in November 1938, Dr. Clifford Williams startled the industry with his address about this new oil industry that more and more "depends on the ability and vision of our research workers and on the highly scientific control of the industrial operations."[21] He also explained that commercial, financial and political acumen alone were no longer a sufficient foundation for the direction of the oil industry. He outlined Shell Development's process for producing from petroleum, a high-quality glycerin in abundance at prices equal to or below those of the natural product. "We have a process which, if necessary, could produce the whole world requirements of glycerine from petroleum gases."

Glycerine was used in nitroglycerin and dynamite, alkyl resins, Du Pont wrapping of cellophane, and in tobacco. The main supplier of natural glycerine had been the soap industry, and prices had fluctuated with the meat industry. After studying the costs that a large glycerine plant would

---

[19] Ibid., p. 541

[20] Ibid.

[21] Ibid., p. 544

entail, which would have to have a long-term contract and be built near enough to that customer (Du Pont) on the East Coast, the plan stalled, and World War II intervened. Finally, in 1948, the plant was started in Houston.

Houston was a logical site, because Shell already had a large refinery there (and none on the East Coast), as well as two chemical plants (the butadiene plant used in the synthetic rubber industry effort was one of these), built in 1941. Chemical companies depend on refineries or other chemical companies as a source of raw materials. And they in turn depend on other chemical companies as customers.

If the industry, and therefore, the citizenry were still not aware of the importance of chemistry in the oil industry, the war years (1939-1945) developed a new appreciation. Chemical processing came to the rescue of manufacturers whose raw materials were no longer available. The industrial research laboratories demonstrated that they were more than able to respond to new problems. The remarkable wartime contributions of the oil company laboratories were the processes they had developed during the Thirties: polymerization, alkylation, catalytic cracking, processes important in aviation gasoline manufacture, methods for making synthetic rubber from butanes and butylenes, etc. etc.[22]

One of the war projects taken on by the industry on behalf of the government was the radar project, which required skills similar to those of a geophysicist. Oil company laboratories took on engine testing for the government, as well as lubricating oil performance under heavy loads, and Shell tested jet-propulsion fuels. They also tested rust inhibitors. Shell's Emeryville lab set to work to improve the method of recovering penicillin. In 1944, the Shell penicillin recovery process was announced, but a latter process was adopted by the pharmaceutical industry.

The most critical materials shortage for the United States during the war was *rubber*. Deprived of 90% of its normal supply of rubber, the U.S. in 1942, began rationing gasoline, as a measure to save tires! Stretching the rubber supply until a new synthetic rubber industry could be built took *two years*. The U.S. public did not know that rubber had been one of the first synthetic materials produced by organic chemists in their laboratories, as far back as 1860. German chemists worked on synthetic rubber at the beginning of the century, and during World War I, the Germans produced several

[22] Ibid., p. 619

tons per day of synthetic rubber made by polymerizing butadiene with sodium. Between the wars, synthetic rubber could not compete in price with natural rubber. However, in the U.S., two oil resistant synthetic rubbers appeared: Thiokol, invented by Dr. J. C. Patrick, and Neoprene, invented by Father Julius Nieuwland of Notre Dame and purchased by Du Pont.

The first country with the incentive for developing an all purpose synthetic rubber was Germany, after Hitler came to power. The German government underwrote the expense, and I. G. Farben started developing Buna-S rubber (the butadiene chain had 25% styrene). In the United States, Standard of New Jersey held the patent rights to Farben's Buna-S rubber. After Congress passed a law, June 1940, to permit the government to purchase and accumulate national stockpiles of key commodities, the Rubber Reserve Company was set up to buy rubber.

Fortunately, stockpiling of rubber did occur before the December 7, 1941, attack on Pearl Harbor by the Japanese. A week later, the U.S. Government swung into action to develop a synthetic rubber industry in the United States. The Roosevelt Administration called to Washington top executives of the oil companies, chemical, and rubber companies, and these companies agreed to share their patents, on a royalty-free basis, and freely exchange technical information on manufacturing techniques.

The process of reacting butadiene and styrene to produce rubber was not too complicated. Styrene was then only produced by Dow Chemical, but other big chemical companies would build and operate the necessary styrene facilities. Butadiene composed around 75% of Buna-S rubber and would come from alcohol and petroleum. A group of oil companies undertook the construction of petroleum based butadiene plants.

Shell was an early supplier of butadiene, because they had built a pilot plant at Emeryville in 1938, producing a ton a day; and early in 1941, Shell Chemical decided to erect a commercial butadiene plant in Houston. It was up and running by November 1941, and during 1942 it was the workhorse of the U.S. synthetic rubber industry, supplying one-third of the country's butadiene. Shell Chemical also built a butadiene plant in Torrance, California, and because Shell was the more experienced, they were continually called upon for technical assistance by the other plants built and operating in the Los Angeles basin, which comprised the West Coast synthetic rubber industry.

Synthetic rubber plants were turning out more rubber than their fabricators could handle by the end of 1944. The future of synthetic rubber from petroleum sources was firmly established!

To service the 50,000 new war planes, Shell shared its 100-octane technology with the rest of the oil industry. Shell's contributions to the war effort were enormous, not only through its researchers, but through the hard work of its engineers in the oilfields and in the various construction and technical tasks. They built storage facilities, laid pipelines, etc., and they improvised.

After World War II, Shell made major advances in offshore technology. The world's first self-positioning drill ship, the *Eureka*, was launched, in 1961, followed by the Bluewater 1, the world's first semi-submersible drilling rig. Also in 1961, Shell developed the first generation of underwater robots controlled from the surface. They are used to install hydraulic lines, turn valves and attach guide lines on the sea floor. In the late 1960s, Shell's geophysicists developed Bright Spot technology, a sophisticated way to read and interpret seismic signals offshore from seismic vessels. Bright Spot has been responsible for many of the new discoveries in the Gulf of Mexico, beginning with the Cognac field in 1,025 feet of water.

Shell has made more major scientific contributions than any other oil company. These contributions spread over different operations of the industry and outside as well, in biological sciences and advanced composite materials technology (e.g. durable polymer concrete), and in alternate energy sources. One of its most applicable, practical contributions for the industry has been in enhanced oil recovery, which Shell first used in Venezuela in the Bolivar Coastal field. In the 1960s and 1970s, Shell experimented with waterflood, steam, and carbon dioxide injection.

Shell produced the first commercial steam-enhanced recovery well at the Yorba Linda field in California, in 1960, and in 1972, pioneered testing of the CO_2 process in West Texas. This was a prelude to the big step that Shell would take in 1979, with its purchase of Belridge Oil Company of California for $3.6 billion, the largest corporate merger to that date. Shell was making a switch to heavier crudes - with the technology to develop these large reserves, and with the investments in upgrading its refineries, to process heavier crudes with a high sulfur content. Once again, Royal Dutch/Shell was leading the oil industry into the future.

As Shell built new refineries, they also built research laboratories with each one, first at Martinez, then Wood River, Houston, and

Wilmington, in the 1930s. Shell Chemical set up research laboratories in connection with its manufacturing activities in Houston, Torrance, and Woodbury, New Jersey, and for agricultural products in Modesto, California. Shell Pipe Line set up a research lab in Houston.

In the 1960s, Shell began to consolidate its research facilities, and after the move of Shell Oil's headquarters to Houston in 1970, the big Westhollow Research Center was built on the outskirts of the city. Emeryville was closed in 1972, before Westhollow opened in 1975. The first major Shell lab built in Houston was the Geophysical Research Laboratory in 1936, which became the Exploration and Production Research Division of Shell Oil in 1945. The new building for the E & P Division was completed in August 1947, and is known as the Bellaire Research Center in Houston.

Shell's emphasis on research has contributed so much to new and better products, as well as Shell's custom of selling its technology, that the company is recognized as an asset in the 100 countries where the Group operates. After 80 years of successfully operating in the United States, few US-Americans realize that Shell Oil Company is a foreign oil company. The Shell Group grants considerable autonomy to its 260 principal operating units, allowing their managers to blend in with their local community and respond swiftly to new regulations and changing customer needs.

Recognition of the importance of research by those at the top, by the holding company, is necessary before you can achieve a credible, successful research program. From the beginning, the Royal Dutch/Shell Group recognized and supported research and set it apart. Support combined with freedom to do research was the key to success. Beginning with Aug. Kessler, Shell researchers have been supported from the top. Shell has not used its research centers as a lateral move for executives when no spot is available in the operating or affiliate companies. This is an important reason why Shell has been so successful in research, compared to other oil companies that do not respect or understand the uniqueness of research. In Exxon, e.g., this habit of finding a slot for an oil executive in a research center is called the "Exxon [ballet] arabesque."

In *Fortune* magazine's annual "Corporate Reputations Survey," January 1991, out of 306 companies in 32 industry groups, Shell Oil ranked the 12th most admired company, and Exxon ranked 82nd. Shell was the highest ranked of any oil and gas company. Good reputations are earned!

Standard Oil of New Jersey (Exxon)

Standard Oil Company (New Jersey), referred to, prior to its name change in 1972 (to Exxon), as Jersey, had accomplished little in the field of new oil technology, prior to 1919. After the break-up of the old Standard Oil Company by the Supreme Court in 1911, Jersey lost the services of the research laboratory at the Whiting Refinery set up in 1886. Jersey also lost the benefit of a new cracking process developed at the lab in 1913. During World War I, supplying the Allies took precedence over new research, but after the war, Jersey's President Walter C. Teagle decided it was time to establish a competent research department under an able executive. Under Frank A. Howard, in 1922, Standard Oil Development Company was formed to carry out and coordinate petroleum research. Howard promptly engaged Warren Lewis of MIT as a consultant.

Research conducted in the U.S. in the mid-nineteenth century was a search for a better illuminant than whale oil and tallow candles. But it was James Young, of Glasgow, Scotland, who first patented a method for extracting a crude liquid from coal and shale. He produced a naphtha (gasoline), a coal oil (kerosene), and lubricants and paraffin wax. In the 1850s, numerous coal oil manufacturers sprang up in cities in the U.S. Their product was kerosene, made from coal. And a few producers and refiners of petroleum, from seepages and salt-water wells, began to market their kerosene product. With the discovery of Edwin Drake's first drilled oil well near Titusville, Pennsylvania, in August 1859, a new industry was created in the United States, and in the world!

Kerosene for illumination was the product sold in the U.S., as a result of the production of the "Oil Regions," the term given to the U.S. producing area. By 1872, U.S. kerosene was being sold in all the major world markets, including Japan, which Admiral Perry had recently opened to Western commerce.

U.S. oilmen were fortunate that Pennsylvania oil was light and low sulfur crude; and that the U.S. Government put a protective duty of 40 cents per gallon on kerosene, in 1861. While they were protected at home, U.S. oilmen could sell around the world, first, kerosene for the literate households, and later, lubricants and greases.

Private mineral rights in the U.S., derived from Anglo-Saxon Common Law, led to over drilling. The "rule of capture," whereby oil belonged to anyone who could gain possession of it through wells drilled on land he owned or leased, prevented producers from adjusting their own production to meet market demand, or the requirements of efficient recovery. Because oil is fugacious, the landowners or leaseholders were encouraged to drill too many wells and they thereby wasted gas and oil pressure. It resulted in a period of flush production followed by rapid decline. Therefore, reservoir research projects were first conducted in the United States, after World War I. They found that the primary lifting agent in the recovery of oil from a reservoir was gas in solution in the oil. With this knowledge, oil companies began to unitize or pool fields.

In the early years, U.S. oilmen borrowed ideas from other industries, e.g., from artesian well drillers, and from modes of transportation. Barrel makers supplied containers suitable for oil transportation.

The *Standard Oil alliance* was formed in 1874, with a group of oilmen joining Ohio Standard, i.e., the leading refiners in New York, Philadelphia, and Pittsburgh joined the Cleveland oilmen headed by John D. Rockefeller. Later, other refiners, pipelines and railroads joined the alliance. Much of their time was spent in fighting other oil groups, such as The Central Association, or the Empire-Pennsylvania combination. The early years of the U.S. oil industry and Standard Oil were spent in cut throat battles between men who had started out as small businessmen.

By 1881, the Standard alliance had captured a large segment of the U.S. petroleum industry, and created a giant combination. Standard Oil dominated the gathering and refining of oil, as well as domestic marketing facilities. At this time, Standard was still not a producer. Rockefeller and his associates wanted to bring the downstream operations "into one commonly owned unit — to create a monopoly."[23] They thus created a giant horizontal and vertical combination in downstream operations.

The evolution of the Standard *Committee system*, which started early, in the 1870s, was the hallmark of its administrative methods. The names of some of their committees were: "Case and Can," "Cooperage" (barrels), "Domestic Trade," "Export Trade," and Manufacturing" (refining).

The Cooperage Committee merits at least a paragraph, or two, on their 1882-1885 activities. This important committee recommended "the

---

[23] Ralph W. Hidy and Muriel E. Hidy, *Pioneering in Big Business- 1882-1911*, History of Standard Oil Company (New Jersey), (New York: Harper & Brothers, 1955) p. 33

standardization of the scale of inter-departmental charges for steam used in the various cooperage establishments," and even more important, what procedures should be used in "gluing and preparing both new and second-hand barrels," as well as the "weight of rivets to be put on hoops," not to mention "the nailing of split barrelheads." "One after another, almost all barreling departments were placed under the supervision of George H. Hooper."[24] At a time when Ludwig Nobel was building more of his tankers and improving the design, Standard was engrossed in gluing barrels. Amazing!

Early research activities for Standard were concentrated in the Cooperage Committee's detailed studies of leakage of export oil, with repeated recommendations to affiliated companies. "Every effort was made to send out oil in leak-proof cans."[25] After several years of study, the Committee "advised all Standard Oil interests shipping export oil to 'double glue' their new barrels." They even set rules on: temperature and quality of glue to be used for each season, a waiting period of three days between the application of the two coats, and the weight of hoops and rivets. Their efforts to improve the barrel as a package were not always successful, particularly in the case of those containing paraffin wax, for candlemakers.

The Standard committee system was the result of the alliance of companies. From the beginning, Standard was a marketing and financial company in New York. (Exxon only recently, in 1990, moved its headquarters out of New York and to the oil patch, to Dallas.) Standard was a refiner and marketer, not an oil producer, and always crude short.

The Standard Oil Trust Agreement was signed, in 1882. Under the Trust, Jersey Standard and Standard Oil Company of New York (Socony) were organized, in 1882. Jersey's functions were "limited to the processing, packaging and sale of products from petroleum and the manufacture of packages and acids."[26] Obviously, Standard of New Jersey was not originally formed to be a producing oil company — and for a long time it was not a producing company. Jersey (Exxon) has always been known as a "crude short" company.

---

[24] Ibid., p. 94

[25] Ibid., p. 142

[26] Ibid., p. 49

Since Standard Oil controlled most of the domestic sales of kerosene, they had about 90% of the kerosene foreign exports. In 1882, U. S. exports had a virtual monopoly on illuminating oil. Standard's only competition was Russian kerosene, which continued to grow, as there was little domestic market for it in Russia. The Russian market was mainly fuel oil for steamships, locomotives and factories. Baku oil contained little sulfur and no paraffin and the derived lubricants surpassed U.S. lubricants in viscosity at low temperatures.

Up to 1886, Standard Oil concentrated on building its empire, and therefore, on marketing techniques. They hoped to keep up or increase the consumption of kerosene for nighttime use. However, George Westinghouse and Thomas Edison were already on the scene and about to change this, first through Westinghouse's introduction of alternating current as a source of power, and Edison's electric light bulb, known as the incandescent lamp. U.S. cities were about to grow and be lit up, but not by kerosene.

Not until July 1886, did Standard do any scientific research. Ohio Standard had to solve the problem of eliminating sulfur from refined oil products, so they hired the "flying Dutchman," Herman Frasch. Frasch had learned the basics of chemistry in the *gymnasium* at Halle, Germany, before immigrating to the U.S., in 1868. He set up his own laboratory, first in Philadelphia, later moved to Cleveland where he continued to invent and patent improved methods of distilling petroleum and manufacturing paraffin. Between 1884 and 1886, Frasch worked on a means of manufacturing kerosene from the sulfurous Ontario crude, similar to the crude in northwestern Ohio (Lima field). Just as with Standard's custom of purchasing oil production and oil companies, it began its research program the same way.

Lima became the focal point of Frasch's research, which was known as the "Herman Experiment." The emergence of the Lima, Ohio-Indiana field yielded a different type of crude, which was ill-smelling (skunk like), sulfur-laden. By 1888, the field was producing more than 35% of all U.S. crude oil. The oil once refined yielded an inferior illuminating oil, and the sulfur caused smoking. Besides yielding a lower quality product, it cost more to refine.

Because Frasch did not quickly live up to Standard's Executive Committee's expectations, Standard decided to promote and sell Lima fuel oil. Thus, a new market was born, and by 1891, Standard Oil had 70% of the new U.S. fuel oil business.

Meanwhile, back in his lab, Frasch finally overcame Lima crude, in October 1888. In order to reduce costs, in 1889, Frasch devised a method and apparatus known as the "Herman Vapor Process," to remove sulfur during primary distillation. However, this process proved cumbersome and expensive. About this time, Standard built the largest refinery (36,000 b/d capacity) in the United States, at Whiting's Crossing, near Chicago. This was the birth of Standard Oil Company (Indiana), in 1889.

Whiting refinery "came to symbolize the victory of Standard Oil over Lima crude and the first large scale fusion of chemical knowledge and practical experience in the American petroleum world."[27] It was a combination of the Herman Experiment and Standard's ample funds available for use when needed! As of December 31, 1891, the Standard Trust had invested more than $32 million in the "Ohio Crude Business." Standard, for the first time, had relied heavily on chemical research (from a German) and engineering skills, for the solution to a problem. Furthermore, they made a great deal of money from Frasch's patents. "That patent monopoly constituted the foundation for the large earnings of several Standard Oil units for more than fifteen years."[28]

In 1989, Amoco (formerly Standard of Indiana) launched a groundwater study of their 100-year old Whiting refinery. As much as 16.8 million gallons of crude oil and petroleum products have seeped into the ground below the refinery complex, and spread to neighborhoods around the refinery. Refineries used to store oil in wooden vessels; and systems for recovering the underground petroleum were either not available or not in place. The seepage is going to cost millions of dollars to clean up!

Jersey's Research Centers

The formation in 1919, of a research department within Jersey Standard, consisted of an information division, a development division, a research laboratory and a patent division. Jersey President Walter Teagle gave the task of organizing a research program to Edgar M. Clark, a scientist and refinery manager at Bayway Refinery, in New Jersey. Clark recruited Frank A. Howard, an engineer and patent lawyer

---

[27] Ibid., p. 165
[28] Ibid., p. 168

in Chicago, to head the new research group, which became Standard Development Company, a wholly owned affiliate in 1922. (The name was changed to the Standard Oil Development Company in 1927, when the engineering department was added.)

The plan under which Standard Oil Development Company had been organized — the so-called Mutual Plan — contemplated the use of the company as a vehicle for coordinating and distributing the cost of all the research and development efforts of general interest to the Jersey affiliates. The formal implementation of this plan was made in 1928 in what was known as the Mutualization Agreement. Under this agreement the other affiliates contracted with Standard Oil Development for the exchange of licenses under patents and for the sharing of the cost of research.[29]

One of the first challenges tackled by the new department was developing a new continuous refining process to increase gasoline yields while using a wide range of crude oil feed stocks. The "tube and tank" cracking process was ready for commercial use in 1921. They also developed isopropyl alcohol, considered to be the first petrochemical, and FLIT, the first petroleum-based household insecticide to be sold commercially.

As the horseless carriage gained in usage and their engines became more powerful, General Motors researchers studied engine knock and identified tetraethyl lead as the most effective anti-knock agent. The Jersey development department chemists developed an inexpensive commercial process for making the anti-knock agent: tetraethyl lead, in 1924. And this invention led to the formation of Ethyl Gasoline Corporation, by Jersey and General Motors, the same year.

In 1927, a new research group was organized and staffed with MIT chemical engineers, at the Baton Rouge refinery — later named the Esso Research Laboratories. The same year, Jersey established contact with a leading German research group, I. G. Farben, which was the most advanced in the world in the chemical research industry. Under a contract with Farben, Jersey undertook to carry out research and development designed to adapt their coal hydrogenation process to oil operations. The new Baton Rouge group went to work on applying hydrogenation to petroleum.

By converting heavy crude into light oil, even gasoline, the MIT group at Baton Rouge accomplished the most important scientific develop-

---

[29] *Horizons 1927-1950*, p. 152

ment in the oil industry! They could also make better lubricants.[30] Ironically, just as Jersey developed this remarkable way of getting more and better products out of oil through hydrogenation, a world oil glut occurred. As Jersey started to construct hydrogenation plants, the East Texas field was discovered. Thus, the new process was useful, but not vital. It cost Jersey $30 million on research and experimental and commercial plants, plus $35 million payment in Jersey stock to I. G. Farben. By 1933, Jersey had reduced its hydrogenation operations to Baton Rouge. However, out of the early experiments was later to come a whole line of important hydrogenation and dehydrogenation processes.[31]

Research on motor oil led to the discovery of Butyl rubber, in 1937. The Jersey scientists were trying to perfect a motor oil thickener when they made the first synthetic Butyl rubber. During World War II, Jersey built Butyl rubber plants under government sponsorship. By the end of the war, Jersey was producing 12 million pounds of Butyl a month. Jersey also developed in 1942, a process to extract butadiene gas from oil. (Butadiene is a raw material for tires.)

Although, the French inventor Eugene Houdry, developed the first commercial catalytic cracking refining process, which revolutionized the oil refining industry, Jersey researchers in 1939, discovered that powdered catalyst behaves like a fluid when mixed with a gas. The Jersey researchers had discovered the fluidized solids reactor bed, better known as the fluid catalytic process. The first commercial fluid catalytic cracker went onstream, in 1942. Catalytic cracking increased the production of high-octane gasoline from a given barrel of oil. It also made it possible to operate the plants at an even temperature.

During the 1940s, Jersey's Standard Oil Development Company opened a research center in Linden, New Jersey, and moved out of its quarters at nearby Bayway Refinery. In 1955, Jersey once more changed its research company's name, from Standard Oil Development, to Esso Research and Engineering Company. Esso Research embarked on the first radiation research in the petroleum industry. Jersey was to move its Engineering research quarters once again, to Florham Park, New Jersey, in 1959.

After World War II, Jersey began opening research organizations abroad: first in England, the Abingdon Research Center of the Esso

---

[30] Ibid., p. 155
[31] Ibid., p. 158

Petroleum Company Ltd.. In 1958, Jersey's international research effort started to expand, e.g., the Esso Harburg Research Center near Harburg, Germany, and the Esso labs at Port Jerome, France, which moved in 1961, to the Mont-Saint-Aignan Research Center near Rouen. Other research centers were built: the Esso Production Research Center at Bordeaux in 1962, and the Fiumicino Research Center near Rome, in 1966 — as well as Esso Chemicals Research Center in Diegem, Belgium.

Today, Exxon has two research companies — Exxon Research & Engineering in New Jersey, and Exxon Production Research in Houston.

Exxon Production Research Company (EPR) in Houston was established in 1964, by merging Humble Production Research (1929) with Jersey Production Research (1937) in Tulsa. EPR is the primary technical arm of Exxon, providing its producing affiliates with the technology needed to explore and produce oil, gas and other hydrocarbons. The three major roles of EPR are: research, research application, and training. With 1,200 employees in 1990 — a professional staff composed of 55% engineering, 26% geoscience, and 54% of the staff with PhDs — EPR is the largest exploration and production research organization in the petroleum industry. The company maintains close contact with Exxon operating affiliates around the world. Through research application, as well as by training of affiliate personnel, EPR technology is transferred to Exxon operations. EPR maintains close contact with Exxon's foreign research organizations in Canada and France, as well as with Exxon's other research company, Research and Engineering Company in Florham Park, New Jersey.

Humble's Geophysicists

Leadership in geophysical techniques used in exploring for oil was provided by a number of companies. However, Humble was the first U.S. company to obtain seismic equipment and staff of its own, on the Gulf Coast, in 1925. The only other companies with seismic crews were from Europe. The three early geophysical instruments used in oil exploration were: the torsion balance, the magnetometer, and the refraction seismograph. Not until the 1920s were these instruments used in the United States. "In sixty years before 1920, sixty-eight major fields

---

[32] *New Horizons 1927-1950,* p. 75

had been discovered."[32]   After 1920, geologists began to replace "practical men" (the unscientific prospectors), and the geologists along with geophysicists found most of the oil fields. By using geophysicists, the equipment and the recording and interpretation of geophysical data also improved. Humble's research group greatly improved the torsion balance, which measures the pull of gravity, and in the 1930s they perfected the first effective gravity meter.

In 1927, Humble assembled a research group to study gas as a factor in oil recovery. Besides learning how gas could be used more efficiently in producing oil from a reservoir, the group studied what ratio of gas to oil obtained from wells in a field would best maintain the reservoir's natural energy and result in the greatest recovery. They learned to space wells to make the most efficient use of the gas to lift the oil and doubled the recoverable oil in a field. And, they demonstrated the savings that could be achieved by the use of a field's natural energy rather than by resorting to pumping.

Next, it was discovered that water was a more important energy source in reservoirs than had previously been realized. The East Texas field was studied as it was developed in the 1930s, and Humble's research engineers studied the possible effect of compressed water beneath the oil in the reservoir. They demonstrated that oil in the East Texas field was driven to the surface principally by the elastic expansion of the compressed water underlying the oil zone.[33]

Standard Oil's affiliates, Humble and Carter, shared their new developments with the other Jersey producing affiliates, as well as with others, through speeches, publications and professional associations. These new reservoir principles greatly improved oil production. They also encouraged Standard to lease large blocks on prospective oil lands, in order to successfully apply their new production technology.

U. S. Joint Research Efforts

here is a long history of joint research efforts between U.S. business and universities. The oldest is between agriculture and higher education. In 1862, Congress passed the Morrill Act, which created public

---

[33] Ibid., p. 83

land-grant institutions that emphasized utilitarian education. These institutions were receptive to the new fields of scientific knowledge. The Hatch Act (1887) and the Smith-Lever Act (1912) funded agricultural research, as well as integrated education, research, and technology transfer. This led to extensive university/business partnerships, and to faculty consulting. And in the 1980s, the so-called "high-tech" industries sprang up, along with the recognition that science and technology are intertwined in significant ways.

The partnerships gave university researchers the opportunity to gain access to excellent industrial laboratories. For business, it was an opportunity to gain access to basic research. Universities conduct more than 60 percent of basic research. Academic research institutions exist primarily to educate students and to discover and share knowledge, while industry exists to produce a product or useful service and provide a return on investment.

A unique example of university and business/industry research joint efforts is the Bureau of Economic Geology at the University of Texas at Austin. The Bureau was established in 1909, and has become one of the largest state geological agencies in the United States. About a dozen major oil companies support applied research projects at the Bureau. Funded largely by industry sources, regional genetic-stratigraphy studies received increased emphasis in hydrocarbon related Bureau projects, in 1989. In 1988, the Geoscience Institute was established at the University and housed at the Bureau. It is a national consortium composed of leading universities and State entities, with advanced oil and gas recovery research programs in petroleum engineering, geophysics, and geology. The Institute programs are base-supported by the U.S. Department of Energy, with cost-sharing from industry, state, and university funds.

The Explosion of Technology

R esearch in drilling has changed and improved drilling technology, making it possible not only to drill deeper wells, but also in deeper water offshore. This drilling research is carried out in large and small laboratories, by majors, independents, and service companies, and in universities, as well as government laboratories, like Sandia Laboratories in Albuquerque. Technological innovations and advances now come from a large variety of companies and research centers. The information age, and the computer, has given us an explosion of new technology in the petroleum industry.

In the 1970s and 1980s great advances were made in drilling. These include: measurement-while-drilling (MWD) tools and techniques; mud-pulse telemetry; downhole drilling motors; long stroke pumps; downhole blowout preventers; pipe handling equipment, such as pipe racking devices used offshore; and making most of this new equipment possible to use: data transmission and controls with computers.

In drill bits, the big breakthrough occurred in polycrystalline diamond compact (PDC) bits, designed to cause the rock to fail in a shearing fashion rather than by compression (which takes more energy). These bits improve penetration rates in many rock types when used with downhole motors. There is a novel drill bit that fires projectiles. A well that required 16 bits to drill in 1955, now only uses two drill bits.

New rigs were built: jack-up rigs, semi-submersible offshore oil drilling rigs, and a specialized, wheeled rig (for the desert). Rigs are now being designed for more specialized applications. In the last 30 years, the science of drilling from floating vessels has developed into a highly complex technology involved in drilling in water depths thousands of feet deep.

Offshore Drilling

The first patent for an offshore oil rig was filed in 1869. In 1894, the first oil well was drilled from a wooden platform off California. Early drilling offshore was from an immobile drilling rig, which was used only once. Later on, the Texas Company (Texaco) built the first submersible rig, which was a barge that could be refloated after completing a well. The new rig was built in Louisiana, in 1934. The first well in open water was put down from a pier a mile offshore from Louisiana, in 1937. Louisiana was to become the most productive offshore area in the United States. Offshore production did not merit the additional costs as long as onshore production was plentiful. Therefore, it was not until after World War II that the oil industry began seriously looking for oil offshore.

The previous paragraph reflects the historical perspective of the U.S. oil industry and is found in books published in the United States, e.g., in Robert O. Anderson's *Fundamentals of the Petroleum Industry*, published in

1984. The U.S. perspective ignores all of the drilling that occurred *in* Lake Maracaibo. The first well in the Lake was drilled in 1923, by Charles R. Eckes with British Equatorial Oil. After this well, Lake Maracaibo was dotted with oil derricks.

With geophysical mapping of offshore areas easier and more sophisticated after World War II, the oil industry began to seriously look in the Gulf of Mexico. Magnetic and seismic surveys from boats were run by geophysicists, just as they did on land. The profiles of the sea bottom, built using specially designed shipboard gravimeters and magnetometers, indicated the vast potential under the Gulf of Mexico.

The U.S. offshore era began in 1947, when the first well beyond sight of land was drilled 12 miles off the Louisiana coast, in water 18 feet deep. Cost of this first offshore platform was $230,000. Today, a platform in the Gulf can operate in water deeper than 1,000 feet, and cost around $1 billion.

Thus, with the great advances in technology, costs have risen, too, because of the challenges encountered. Working conditions are formidable in deeper water: rigs must withstand hurricane winds, ice floes (a real danger in the Labrador Alley), strong currents, wave action, inhospitable bottom conditions, submarine pressures, and mud flows (Mississippi River mud in the Gulf of Mexico).

In the past 30 years, the science of drilling from floating vessels has developed to drilling in water depths of 5,000 feet, with all the safety, control, and capability available to land-based operations. The industry's most sophisticated rigs have been designed to operate in 5,000 to 6,000 feet of water. At least one-third of all undrilled leases in the Gulf of Mexico in 1990, were beneath 3,000 feet, or more, of water. There are 18 rigs with a 3,000 ft depth capability worldwide, excluding those used by Petrobras in Brazil's offshore, according to *Offshore* magazine, October 1990. This deepwater drilling fleet was built between 1975 and 1989. Shell Offshore continues to be the leader in deepwater drilling technology. Petrobras had the largest deepwater drilling program (in the Campos Basin), worldwide, in 1990. A May 1990 issue of *Offshore* states that over 700 offshore fields outside the U.S. are slated for development between 1990 and 1995.

There are two accompanying areas of development in other industries that have made possible offshore deepwater drilling and production. The first is a new generation of floating cranes. A Dutch company,

Heerema, was a major pioneer in developing heavy-lift technology in the 1970s. In 1978, Heerema introduced the *Balder*, a semi-submersible heavy-lift vessel, followed by a sister vessel, the *Hermond*. Another breakthrough came in 1982, when two cranes were successfully used one in front of the other (in tandem). By introducing revolving cranes, the lifting weights increased, and topside modules of 2,000 tons could be installed on offshore platforms. Tandem crane lifts opened the way to greater lifting capacity to 7,000 and 9,000 tons, even to 14,000 tons.

The cost savings using heavy lift technology were enormous in building an offshore platform. By lifting the jacket, you save the need to strengthen the platform specifically for the launch, which would only be necessary for the few minutes of the launch. And testing platform decks onshore minimizes the work necessary for an offshore hook-up.

The second important development in another industry that contributed to deepwater drilling is the helicopter. Particularly, in the Gulf of Mexico where deepwater exploration activity can be 100 to 200 miles from shore, the helicopter is essential for equipment deliveries, for crew rotation, quick evacuation in the event of a disaster, or rapid evacuation in the face of an approaching hurricane. Helicopter operators are changing strategies to expand overseas, as U.S. major oil companies expand their operations to include Latin America and countries in the Eastern Hemisphere. In 1982, there were 870 helicopters in the U.S. Gulf Coast. The industry suffered the downturn of the oil industry in the 1980s, and the number left in 1990, was 600. In 1990, therefore, there was a shortage of copters, for the first time in ten years, and new helicopters were being ordered from Bell Helicopter Textron.

Horizontal Drilling

Horizontal drilling is an old idea dating back to the 1890s and first tried in the late 1920s. In the 1950s, 43 wells were drilled in the U.S.S.R., but were uneconomic. The economic gap between vertical and horizontal drilling began to close in 1986, and in the years since. Horizontal drilling is now being used as a result of a breakthrough in micro-electronics, which makes it possible to use instruments having integrated circuits within drill collars. The new drilling techniques being used are: measurement while drilling (MWD), downhole motors, and slotted liner completions. Computers help guide the drilling process as the pipe containing the motorized drill bit curves toward the horizontal direction. The well pipe does not rotate, only the drill bit. In the traditional vertical drilling, the well pipe rotates with the bit.

Horizontal drilling should not be confused with directional drilling, which is normally used to drill multiple wells from a single surface location, or to reach bottomhole targets that cannot be reached from a particular surface location by a vertical well. The main purpose of horizontal drilling is to increase production rates, and ultimate recovery.

Horizontal penetration connects isolated pockets of fractured reservoirs, and thus the well is able to intersect and drain as many fractures as possible. In the past seven years, horizontal drilling has become a permanent fixture of the oil and gas industry. It was first applied commercially outside the United States, French owned Elf Aquitaine was a leader, with wells in Italy. However, it has taken hold in the U.S. because of improvements in technology, environmental factors and a need by oil companies to cut costs. Eastman Christensen (bought by Baker Hughes) has concentrated research time and money in the short-radius systems of horizontal drilling. The biggest problem wasn't the drilling, but the lack of completion tools. Completion technology was three years behind the drilling technology. The close cooperation needed, between service companies and oil companies, to successfully drill horizontal wells, is changing the way the oil industry does business. It has brought the industry closer together. Horizontal wells are more expensive to drill then vertical wells - but if successful they can greatly increase production flow.

Oryx Energy Co. was the leader in horizontal drilling in the U.S., where it set out in the mid-1980s, to increase production in the Pearsall field, in the Texas Austin Chalk Trend. Drilling in the field had peaked in 1976-77, and had declined to an average of 5 b/d per well. One of its new horizontal wells was the Heitz No. 1, which achieved a horizontal reach of 2,860 feet at a depth of 8,910 feet, and production tests of 3,200 b/d.

Worldwide interest in horizontal drilling has led to the largest jointly funded drilling research project in the industry's history. About 95 oil companies and service companies are participating in Drilling Engineering Association - 44. Participants are from 18 countries, and the aims of the project are: development of personal computer programs related to drilling, completion, production, and reservoir engineering, technology transfer, and a literature search.

Horizontal drilling is predicted to yield a major increase in world hydrocarbon recovery. About 250 horizontal wells were drilled in 1989. The number is expected to rise every year, and account for about 20% of world drilling. In the future gas reservoirs may hold wider application potential for horizontal wells than oil reservoirs.

In 1990, a new high-tech twist to horizontal drilling was added in Texas. Called dual-leg drilling, the advance has been tested successfully in the prolific Austin Chalk. Just as the horizontal well begins as a vertical well and then at about 6,000 feet angles sideways to form a 90-degree angle, so too does the dual-leg horizontal well with the addition of a second angle running in the opposite direction. The two sides are drilled with separate bits. In the U.S., there is a leasing problem with dual leg drilling. Many leases are not long enough to accommodate the span of dual leg wells.

Petroleum Geochemistry

As oil became more difficult to find, the geologist needed an understanding of the geochemistry of petroleum. Perhaps the first geochemist was T. Sterry Hunt, a Canadian. Hunt elaborated on a theory of how petroleum originated by slow decomposition of organic matter, which a German chemistry professor at Bonn, Karl G. Bischof, had proposed. In 1863, Hunt defined the lower forms of marine life as the probable sources of petroleum. Many geologists had a chemical understanding of oil. Geologists now know that hydrocarbons are found in practically all sedimentary rocks. And Wallace E. Pratt, of Humble Oil and Refining Co., (a Standard of Jersey affiliate) described, in his 1941 University of Kansas lectures, that small molecules are formed from large molecules through natural cracking at depth. The decreasing molecule size is concurrent with the increasing hydrogen-to-carbon ratio.

In petroleum exploration and development of a field, the geologist, engineers, and geophysicists characterize an exploration or development objective in terms of structural configurations, rock, or pressure decline. Petroleum geochemists address hydrocarbon fluids in the reservoirs, and integrate the geochemical data into the geological framework and production history of a field. Geochemists focus on determining the number of genetic oil types in an area, and try to predict the number and character of the source beds.

Modern organic geochemistry started some 35 years ago with Standard Oil of New Jersey's affiliate, Carter Oil in Tulsa, Oklahoma, and the Royal Dutch/Shell Group in Rijswijk, Holland. Applied geochemistry was mostly limited to the major oil companies that set up their own analytical laboratories, which were staffed by analytical chemists, geologists and technicians. A number of geochemical service companies offering a full compliment of services to the oil industry sprang up after 1970. Universities have also carried out substantial research in geochemistry, as well as teaching courses up to the doctorate level.

What does a geochemist do? His search begins with the origin of oil and gas. He studies the generation, migration, and accumulation of liquid and gaseous hydrocarbons below ground. A geochemist delineates between potentially favorable source facies and stratigraphically relatable organic facies, and defines the depths at which optimum thermal digenetic conditions prevail for the formation of oil and gas. This simply means that the geochemist defines how petroleum is formed, where it is located, at what depths, and how it migrated from fine-grained source rock into porous reservoir facies.

Geochemists define mineralogical changes that can be attributed to heat and pressure as metamorphic. The end products of all sedimentary organic matter are methane and graphite. Perhaps 80 to 95% of all petroleum hydrocarbons form from the thermal transformation of kerogen with temperature and time.[34] In the origin of petroleum, the most important factor is the thermal history of the source rock.

> The science of petroleum geochemistry is the application of chemical principles to the study of the origin, migration, accumulation, and alteration of petroleum, and the use of this knowledge in exploration and recovery of oil, gas, and related bitumens.[35]

Surface hydrocarbon geochemical prospecting is the measurement and the interpretation of infinitesimally small quantities of microseeping

---

[34] John M. Hunt, *Petroleum Geochemistry and Geology* (San Francisco: W. H. Freeman & Co., 1979), pp. 143-144
[35] Ibid., p. 3

hydrocarbons sampled in the near-surface soil, directly or nearly directly, over an oil field, according to Dr. Martin Davidson, of Dallas. In 1929, at the Max Planck Institute in Berlin, the first on-going research occurred, and was expanded in the Soviet Union by V. A. Sokolov by 1932. The first geophysical research laboratory in the United States was in Houston, established in the early 1930s, by Dr. Ludwig Blau, as part of the Standard Oil Development Company. However, in spite of its success there is limited use of surface geochemical prospecting, today, due to a scientific controversy with reflection seismic. Patillo Higgins would not be surprised by the controversy in exploration. Scientific data may change but not man's nature.

Dr. John Hunt, in his book on *Petroleum Geochemistry and Geology*, points out that only in this century has technological capability been developed to obtain the enormous quantities of fossil fuel now required to meet the energy demands of the world's expanding economy. To meet these energy demands will require the ingenuity of the petroleum exploration geologists, geophysicists, geochemists and the drilling and production engineers. They are now aided by micropaleontology, heavy minerals, the electrical log, the reflection seismograph, the air-borne magnetometer, clay-mineral transformations, the stratigraphic trap, the new global tectonics, the bright spot, and the thermal window. With all this help, oilmen should be able to locate petroleum, the second most abundant fluid in the earth's crust after water.

Research in the oil industry moves in a circle, from the upstream operations of exploration, development, and production to the downstream operations of transportation and refining. Collaboration among companies was often essential when problems were very large. Research in academic institutions was followed closely, and geologists, engineers and chemists often staid in close contact with their alma maters.

> Institutionalized research and development carried on by a large organization had become essential in the 1930s in an industry where progress in technology required large resources of highly trained men and capital. The day of the lone inventor and innovator was all but gone. (*New Horizons*, p. 175)

This then is the history and the milieu of research into which Intevep sprang after its creation, to begin to make its contributions to modern technology. ●

CHAPTER II

INTEVEP'S CREATION— THE GIANTS CLASH

B efore there was Intevep there was Invepet!
Invepet probably had many more founding fathers than
Intevep because it was a grassroots effort of many different groups
outside of the foreign oil industry. Regardless of the approach one
uses to determine the beginning of Intevep (**Venezuelan Institute of
Petroleum Technology**), it becomes self-evident that Intevep was the
culmination of the efforts of several distinguished Venezuelan scientists,
and one in particular — Marcel Roche — and the efforts of university professors, Venezuelan oilmen, and politicians.

In 1969, **Marcel Roche, M.D.**, was appointed President of the new
National Science and Technology Research Council **(CONICIT)**, and the
next year CONICIT included petroleum in its priorities. The **Petroleum**

Working Group was formed in May 1970, and headed by Dr. Roche. The Group recommended the creation of a Venezuelan Petroleum and Petrochemical Research Institute (Invepet), and that CONICIT **in the interim** form a petroleum and petrochemical research **commission,** which the Board approved, in March 1971.

The report of the Working Group is a well written, brief, to-the-point summary of the problem. It points out that the oil industry was in the hands of foreigners, and they had limited their efforts to extraction for export of large volumes of crude, therefore, there was no motivation to develop research facilities in Venezuela. The report noted that the lack of Venezuelan researchers, in an industry that in 1969 accounted for 93% of Venezuela's exports and 89% of total foreign currency, was a serious economic problem. The report also pointed out that Venezuela was the largest exporter of oil in the world. However, it did not point out that Venezuela had four large export refineries (Jersey, Shell, Gulf, and Mobil), and that their main export product was residual oil, which largely went to the U.S. and sold for less than the price for crude oil.

Marcel Roche also headed the **Petroleum and Petrochemical Research Commission,** and Anibal Martinez was the coordinator. Many of the same members of the Working Group were on the Commission. Among these members were: Dr. Roche and Mr. Martinez, Dr. Paulino Andreu, Humberto Calderon Berti, Jose Martorano Battisti, and Ulises Ramirez. Dr. Nestor Barroeta and Winston Peraza were on the Commission but not on the Working Group. It was clear to the 13-member CONICIT **Commission** that Venezuela particularly needed research capabilities in heavy oil, since its largest reserves are in heavy oil and bitumen. The Commission met between 1971 and 1973, and identified the principal research needs of the Venezuelan petroleum industry and prepared a project for the founding of Invepet, and recommended the formation of IMPELUZ, and supported the creation of the Department of Petroleum and Petrochemicals at IVIC.

But how was a petroleum institute to be formed? The small national oil company, Corporacion Venezolana de Petroleo (CVP), supported the idea, but among the foreign oil companies only oilmen from Shell gave it any support or interest. The Working Group had recommended that initially university facilities should be utilized (and increased) along with other research institutes.

Invepet was created by President Rafael Caldera's (1969-1974) presidential decree No. 1385, in August 1973, and was formed in *February 1974*, as the **Foundation for Research in Hydrocarbons and Petrochemicals.**. The founding group of 40 professionals from the oil industry, the Ministry of Mines and Hydrocarbons, and CONICIT, and headed by Humberto Calderon Berti, who was the Director of Reversion in the Ministry, set up its first office in the Centro Empresarial Miranda in Los Ruices, Caracas. They organized committees composed of inter-company Venezuelan oilmen, and officials from the Ministry of Mines, to study the foreign transfer of technology to the concessionaire companies in Venezuela. Most of the technology used by the petroleum industry in Venezuela came from foreign sources, i.e., from the research centers of the foreign oil companies.

The **Invepet report on technology transfer** within the petroleum industry, known as, Diagnostico Sobre Tranferencia Tecnologica de la Industria Petrolera, covered exploration, production, refining, and computer technology. It was presented to the government of Carlos Andres Perez (1974-1979), in April 1975. If nationalization was to take place later that year, Invepet had a blueprint for the oil industry's weaknesses and strengths in technology.

Invepet was the result of the efforts, over several years, of a few concerned Venezuelan scientists with political power and a few oilmen, who realized that Venezuela needed its own petroleum research center. Once the Reversion Law was passed in July 1971 (whereby oil concessions would revert back to the Venezuelan government in 1983-1984, as well as refineries and assets outside of the concession areas), and the debate commenced about "after" nationalization, it became clear that Venezuela could not afford to annually spend millions of dollars for technical assistance contracts (CATs).

Among the good things the foreign oil companies did while they had concessions in Venezuela was to train, educate, and promote capable Venezuelans. Even some of Venezuela's most prominent scientists had been educated abroad with scholarships from the oil companies, particularly through the Creole Foundation (Exxon). Thus, at the time of nationalization in 1975, there was a very capable core of Venezuelan oilmen to takeover. Most important for success, the Venezuelan oilmen had the esprit de corps (called *mistica* in the Venezuelan industry), to form an efficient, farsighted industry, **and** the assistance of a new research institute to help the Venezuelan oil, gas, and petrochemical industry to grow!

About the same time that Invepet was formed and was working on its master plans, and feasibility studies (lubricant and additive laboratories, and geophysical data processing center), a group of researchers, at the Instituto Venezolano de Investigaciones Cientificos **(IVIC)**, in Los Teques, which Raimundo Villegas, M.D., was Director of then, joined the newly created **Petroleum and Petrochemical Center**, in June 1973. This had been one of the suggestions of the Petroleum Commission. The purpose of the center was: research in oil refining and petrochemical products, chemical research, technical service to the national industry, and graduate studies. Part of this group of 123 was later transferred to **Intevep** (78 moved), in July 1977. Intevep would thus obtain a solid core of researchers from IVIC, headed by Dr. Nestor Barroeta.

Why were prominent Venezuelans so concerned about research in the oil industry? Surely, with new technology that was developed in Venezuela over the years, the foreign oil companies had set up laboratories in Venezuela. They did set up small labs in the early years. However, when they began to build their large expensive research laboratories in the United States they closed down most of their small overseas labs.

The traditional oil products lab, which was an outgrowth of a refinery, were not built in Venezuela because the oil companies did not build large refineries in Venezuela — until after the death of Juan Vicente Gomez (1935), who did not want refineries in Venezuela, and after the Medina Government's Hydrocarbon Law of 1943 obliged them to build refineries (more in the following chapter). In the early years, foreign oil companies only had small topping plants to cover their individual needs and supply nearby towns. Thus, the small labs that the foreign oil companies built in Venezuela were for research **in** exploration and upstream operations, and not for downstream operations.

Oil Company Laboratories in Venezuela

P an American Petroleum's subsidiary in Venezuela, Lago Petroleum Co., set up a "laboratory" at the company's Maracaibo office, which Hollis D. Hedberg joined, in 1926. The "lab" was a 6 x 15-foot cell below ground level, beneath a small garage building. Dr. Hedberg had one "cell mate," Dr. Bill Hoffmeister, who also had just arrived from the United States. Dr. Hedberg was hired as a petrographer and Dr. Hoffmeister as a paleontologist. During these early years there were few well core samples, and Dr. Hedberg had to rely on ditch samples for the Bolivar Coastal fields. However, his persistence soon paid off, and it became clear that "below the Upper Tertiary mottled claystones, the Lagunillas and La Rosa formations with their producing oil sands, . . . many of the wells reached an underlying indurated gray . . . shale and sandstone unit." [1] Dr. Hedberg's early work in Venezuela confirmed the existence of a major unconformity in the Bolivar Coastal Fields.

After joining Venezuelan Gulf Oil in 1929, Dr. Hedberg moved on to field work. This work in connection with the reputation of the Maracaibo Gulf laboratory for both heavy mineral and micropaleontology "led most of the smaller companies of the region to bring their well samples to Gulf for study, which was of great mutual benefit to both parties." [2]

Creole created a "corrosion group," which conducted experiments at La Salina with the aid of Clapp Marine Biological Laboratory. The Lake presented major technical problems in oil production that were caused by: high salinity of the water; the *teredo*, a water-born termite that destroyed virtually any protective coating applied to prevent corrosion; "bear hair;" and other aquatic vegetation that clogged pumps and filters. Not until the 1960s did Creole discover plastic coatings capable of warding off both *teredos* and corrosion.

Shell set up a small laboratory in Maracaibo, in 1939. Shell used palynology, i.e., pollen and spores, for the first time in oil exploration, in 1939. The Shell Group is famous for its production of heavy oil using "huff and puff" recovery methods, which it developed in the Bolivar Coastal fields.

In 1945, Mene Grande (Gulf) started the Geological Department's laboratory in Caracas. Many employees were transferred from Maracaibo, and several new foreign staff were added.

An interesting and nearly forgotten chapter of the history of oil research in Venezuela is the contribution of the pioneers who invented as

---

[1] Hollis D. Hedberg, "Geological Reminiscences of my early years in Western Venezuela," *Boletin*, Sociedad Venezolana de Geologos, No. 34, Caracas, December 1988, pp. 70-78

[2] Ibid., p. 74

they encountered problems. The oilmen who came to Venezuela in the early days, in the 1920s and 1930s, were individually quite inventive. **For example:**

Joe Holmes, a Lago supervisor (who later went on to be President of International Petroleum Co., which owned half of Mene Grande), worked on an idea to protect the wood pilings used in the Maracaibo Lake wells, from the *teredo* that was destroying the pilings. He dipped the wood in a bath filled with creosote, and finding that creosote would not soak into the wood, he resorted to forcing it into the wood by pressure. This slowed down the terrible teredos, but the final solution was left to young George McCammon with his concrete pilings, in 1933.

There was John Taylor, also with Lago, who was given the job of mapping the bottom of the Lake. First, he made a survey of the Lake, drawing straight lines a kilometer apart, from north to south. But how could he measure the depth of the water along the lines? His solution was ingenious. Using a motor launch with two working crews, one on either side, and the launch captain with a big clock with a big minute hand, while maintaining a steady speed and blowing his whistle every minute, the crews alternated taking soundings. The two foremen sang out the measurements and Taylor wrote them down. It took them over six months in 1927, to complete the map, which the Venezuelan government checked, and accepted as the official map of Lake Maracaibo!

But perhaps the cleverest inventor was Jimmy Childress, Lago's master mechanic, who before arriving in Venezuela had worked in numerous places from Texas to Casablanca. Childress could invent almost anything Lago needed — and sketch it out on his penny box of matches with a stub of a pencil. He could not draw or read blueprints, but he could squeeze all of his ideas on a matchbox, as he did with the steel drilling barge he designed, in 1932. This led to building the lake barges in Venezuela. Later, Childress sketched out on his matchbox the plans for a pipe-laying barge, which made laying pipelines in the Lake almost as easy as on the shore.

Offshore drilling and producing was started in Lake Maracaibo. Lago men opened up one of the world's greatest treasures for the benefit of Man. Their ingenuity set a pattern other men would follow in the Gulf of Mexico, and elsewhere. The giant drilling barges now in use offshore around the world are similar to the one that Jim Clark conceived of and

Jimmy Childress drew on the back of a matchbox. Thus, these foreigners in Venezuela pioneered offshore drilling, and developed new technology in their "outdoor labs".

Those foreigners also developed an outstanding technical innovation — the large capacity over-water gas conservation plant. Gas conservation, by the early 1950s, had become a matter of increasing concern for Creole and Venezuelans. The fields to be served were extensive and produced immense volumes of natural gas. Creole with the help of Ingersoll-Rand and Cooper-Bessemer began to explore using centrifugal compression and turbine power. On January 15, 1955, after four years of study and 18 months of construction, the **first** installation of a gas conservation plant, **Tia Juana I**, was dedicated. These gas plants augmented oil production by increasing pressure, and eliminated the flaring of natural gas, and permitted extensive use of gas-lift as an oil production technique in lieu of the more traditional lift with pumping jacks.

The First Venezuelan Scientists

I n Venezuela, **physicians** have played a key role in scientific development. There are several reasons for this: tropical diseases were an important concern; there were no higher degree granting universities until the middle of this century; and the elite who attended the university chose either medicine, law or political science, for there were few other choices. And one can add another reason: Venezuelans have always had high regard for what was foreign made or invented. (There would seem to be a missing article in the Venezuelan Constitution that states that every Venezuelan has the right to travel abroad, often!) Medical degrees were granted by the Central University, but no Masters or Ph.D. degrees. Furthermore, most prominent physicians studied in Europe (mainly Paris, because of Louis Pasteur, 1822-1895, the French chemist who was the founder of modern bacteriology), or in the United States, during some period of their training.

The first scientific research institute in Venezuela was started in Maracaibo in **1884**, and was headed by Dr. Rafael Lopez Baralt. It was located next to the Hospital de Chiquinquira, and it did experiments in physiology, anatomy, chemistry and general medicine.

Later, it was decided to install a research institute in Caracas and **Dr. Jose Gregorio Hernandez** was sent to Paris to study the most advanced experimental medicine of the nineteenth century. With the laboratory equipment that Dr. Hernandez brought back from Paris, a laboratory was opened at the Hospital Vargas in **November 1891**, for the study of bacteriology and physiology.

According to Marcel Roche, professional research started in Venezuela in **1902**, when **Rafael Rangel** took charge of the Laboratory (Jose Gregorio Hernandez's) at the Hospital Vargas, Caracas' famous public hospital, named after Dr. Jose Vargas, which was opened January 1, 1891. In 1991, the Hospital Vargas celebrated its 100-year anniversary. It was indeed appropriate that the first public teaching hospital in Caracas, the Hospital Vargas, was named after the doctor that founded medical science in Venezuela.

Most important things in Venezuela are done by presidential decree and published in the *Gaceta Oficial*, and so was the Hospital Vargas, on August 16, 1888. It was the end of the old colonial tradition of alms "for the love of God" for the sick, and the beginning of collectively taking care of the poor who were sick. The nursing staff at Hospital Vargas started with 18 French nuns from the Congregation of San Jose de Tarbes. (The San Jose de Tarbes nuns were brought to Venezuela by the grandfather of Jack Tarbes, who became President of Lagoven in 1984. They ran **the** girls school in Caracas, located in the former home of the President of Venezuela, Raimundo Andueza Palacio, in El Paraiso.) The Hospital Vargas was the idea of Dr. Calixto Gonzalez, who went on to teach some of Venezuela's practicing doctors and teachers, and one **Jose Gregorio Hernandez,** who in turn taught **Rafael Rangel**, who was Venezuela's best researcher at the beginning of the twentieth century.

Jose Gregorio Hernandez and Rafael Rangel were great doctors and saintly men; both were heroes in their time. Jose Gregorio was put up for Beatification in the Catholic Church, by the Archbishop of Caracas, in June 1950. Some in Venezuela pray to him. Rafael Rangel, whom Marcel Roche, in his book about Rangel, describes as having virtues common to very few men, in his service to Man, and "would have been a saint" in the Middle Ages (p. 316), could never be Canonized because he committed suicide. Dr. Roche raises the disturbing questions about the acceptance of researchers in Venezuela.

Dr. Rangel was a man who had excellent grades in school, but instead of seeking a profession where he could make lots of money and become socially prominent, he chose the life of research with a modest salary. His work was original, without letup, producing papers that are models of scientific prose. He was always open to requests and immensely generous, particularly with his students. Rangel was the exception among Venezuela's great doctors, for he never traveled abroad, even though the National Academy of Medicine awarded him a grant to study in Europe, in 1905. Nevertheless, Rangel learned four additional languages to Spanish. He died very young, at 32. Marcel Roche ends his book on Rafael Rangel, published in 1973, with the following:

> For those of us who are convinced that the country should be oriented — though not necessarily governed — by thinkers, scientists, creators in general, without consideration of their origin, of their fortune, or other external or accidental circumstances, Rangel, and men like him, constitute the **true elite.**

Another important laboratory and doctor was the Pasteur Institute of Caracas, founded in April 1895, by a group of five medical doctors headed by **Santos Dominici.** It was the first clinical laboratory in Venezuela and was privately funded by businessmen in Caracas, and the doctors themselves. This institute, created just seven years after the Pasteur Institute in Paris, begins closer medical ties with Europe and the world. They were able to duplicate and develop discoveries made elsewhere, and thus to "transfer technology" rapidly. (Roche, *Rafael Rangel*, p.79) Unfortunately, the Pasteur Institute only lasted seven years, as politics again intervened. The Director, Santos Dominici, had to go into exile, as he was opposed to the government of Cipriano Castro (1899-1908), and with his departure the Institute closed, in 1902.

But the most remarkable Venezuelan medical doctor remains, **Dr. Jose Maria Vargas,** born in 1786, in La Guaira, when Venezuela was still a Spanish colony. He studied in Europe during the Wars for Independence, and returned to a liberated Venezuela, where he became Rector of the Central University and the first doctor to hold that position. In 1835, Dr. Vargas became President of Venezuela, for a few months, i.e., until a military government took power and shipped him off to the Virgin

Islands. However, he returned to the presidency when the rebels were overthrown by General Jose Antonio Paez who had been President before Vargas. In April 1836, President Vargas resigned and returned to medicine and the University. He was an important part of the founding of Venezuela — contributing to the development of education.

Dr. Vargas is called the Founder of Medical Science in Venezuela. At the University, he created the Anatomy, Surgery, and Chemistry Departments, wrote the texts for their courses, and donated funds, libraries and museums to the University. He was honored with Venezuela's highest tribute: in 1877, his remains were entombed in the Nacional Panteon where Simon Bolivar and the founding fathers (and mother, Luisa Caceres de Arismendi) are buried. Dr. Vargas had died in New York in 1854, where he went for medical treatment, and his body was returned to Venezuela in 1877.

Clinica Luis Razetti, which opened in 1911, was the first private clinic in Caracas to perform surgery and care for these patients. The clinic was started by **Dr. Luis Razetti** (1862-1932), the great educator, reformer, and traveler, who is also buried in the National Panteon.

The next exceptional Venezuelan hospital opened 40 years later, in 1951, the Clinica El Avila, served by the Spanish nuns of San Jose. Another hospital of note in Caracas was built and equipped by Shell Oil, known as Centro Medico, in San Bernardino. It opened around 1950. Not only could babies be safely born and patients operated on and cared for in these hospitals, research could also be performed in their laboratories.

The most far-reaching battle ever won in Venezuela was not fought with guns. The success of the fight against malaria may be best appreciated by the fact that up to 1936, malaria was the primary cause of death in Venezuela. **Dr. Arnoldo Gabaldon**, head of the Malaria Division from 1936 till 1950, prevailed upon the Ministry of Health and Social Welfare, to create this separate agency for the fight against malaria. Ways and means to combat the disease were devised by Dr. Gabaldon. He supervised the research work, trained the men to go into the field — in fact, his organization became a model in the fight against malaria.

For many years, Venezuela has had a number of excellent scientists, with international recognition through their publications. But Venezuela has not had the research facilities these researchers deserved and the country needed to advance research. Certainly, **Baruj Benacerraf**, born in Caracas in 1920, would never have received the Nobel Prize in Medicine and Physiology in 1980, for his contribution to modern immunology, if he had not gone to France, and then to the United States for his M.D., and then to Columbia University, back to Paris for 6 years, then to New York University School of Medicine, later to the National Institute of Health, and finally to Harvard Medical School. Dr. Benacerraf, whom Marcel Roche called Venezuela's most illustrious researcher in modern science, would have had a difficult time reaching his goals if he'd staid in Venezuela.

A study of Venezuela's scientific development was started by Olga Gasparini for IVIC in 1967, and published in 1969, with the title, *La investigacion en Venezuela: Condiciones de su desarrollo.* She found that there were around 1,800 researchers in Venezuela, but only 600 had published more than two articles on their work, and only 16% were dedicated exclusively to research. Furthermore, one third of the researchers were born abroad, and 97% did their graduate work abroad.

Dr. Roche points out that while science is admired and has prestige in Venezuela, the scientist is not admired. Today, it is possible that there are some 4,000 researchers in Venezuela, with those who publish found mainly at the Central University, IVIC, Intevep, Simon Bolivar University, the University of the Andes in Merida, and the University of Zulia.

At the turn of the century, groups of university professors encouraged the creation of national academies. Thus, the **creation of academies preceded the existence of scientific research** as a professional activity. And Venezuelan academies were created by the government, with a constant number of members, and acted as advisers to the government.

After World War II, Venezuela encouraged European immigration and among those who came to Venezuela were university professors to train Venezuelan students, at the Central University of Venezuela, in Caracas. In 1950, Francisco De Venanzi, M.D., and a group of researchers and professors at the University founded the Venezuelan Association for the Advancement of Science (AsoVAC).

In 1952, Luis Roche, the large land developer, and his son, Marcel Roche, M.D., created the **Institute of Medical Research** (IIM), better known as the Roche Foundation. This distinguished group of medical doctors was led by Dr. Roche, and included: Francisco De Venanzi, M.D., who became the Rector of the Central University and was highly regarded and loved; Miguel Layrisse, M.D., who was later President of CONICIT and Vice-President of Invepet; Tulio Arends, M.D., hematologist, and later Minister of State—President of CONICIT, now deceased; and Luis Carbonell, M.D., who later became Director of IVIC, and Minister of State—President of CONICIT. This was the first basic research group in Venezuela, and after 1958 would take over IVNIC, along with Gabriel Chuchani, Karl Gaede, Gernot Bergold and Gunnar Svaetrichin, to form IVIC.

Venezuelan Institute of Neurological and Brain Research (IVNIC)

A research center was created atop Altos Pipe (Pipe Mountain), in 1955, at the instigation of **Humberto Fernandez-Moran, M.D.**, University of Munich, and **Ph.D.** in biophysics from the University of Stockholm. In 1947, Dr. Fernandez-Moran joined the Nobel Institute for Physics where he began his work in **electron microscopy**. At the Nobel Institute he developed the **diamond knife** (U.S. Patent No. 3,060,781). Dr. Fernandez-Moran said that it was in Sweden where he learned methodology, and about time. "The Swedes are not out to do things on deadlines," he often told friends. "In Sweden I had the inside track into the hospitals, as a doctor; into their science, through the Nobel Institute; into the politics, economics, the social life, as cultural attache. I wanted to learn these things to take home to Venezuela with me." In 1954, he returned to Venezuela to study tropical medicine — the role of viruses and insects — and continue his lifetime work on the fine structure of the nervous system through electron microscopy.

Under the government of Marcos Perez Jimenez (1952-1958), Dr. Fernandez-Moran was authorized to develop a $50 million national center for research in neurology and brain physiology, the **Venezuelan Institute of Neurological and Brain Research** (IVNIC). Fernandez-Moran conceived of it as a regional research center for all of South America, which would also develop into an international training center. IVNIC's charter was dated April 29, 1954, as an *autonomous* institute.

Unfortunately, he chose scientists from abroad, primarily Europe, to work at IVNIC, and alienated Venezuelan scientists from the beginning.

Dr. Fernandez-Moran selected Pipe, a 5,000-foot mountain, seven miles from Caracas, to build the institute. The site was selected from the air. The author's cousin, Air Force Captain Guillermo Hernandez Jacobsen, M.D., flew his friend Humberto over the foothills surrounding Caracas until Humberto found the right spot. When they were suiting up to take off in the Air Force plane, Humberto turned to Guillermo and asked him what he should do if they had to bail out and his parachute did not open. "Llame a Maria" (Call the Virgin Mary), Guillermo answered.

The mountain top was flattened after Fernandez-Moran took title to Pipe, January 1, 1955, and by December 2 there was a $3 million pilot unit waiting for General Perez Jimenez to inaugurate. (Each year after December 2, 1952, when Perez Jimenez overturned the elections he had called for, making voting compulsory, and then lost and named himself President of Venezuela, he dashed all over Venezuela on December 2, inaugurating buildings, schools, hospitals, hotels and highways. This was the greatest building period in Venezuelan history — what was started was finished — on time.) In 11 months IVNIC had a building that housed six institute departments, a workshop, three electron microscopes and a library; staff residences; an 800-kw electric power station, and a water supply system with a six-million liter artificial lake.

But IVNIC was to become much more. In 1955, when he was overseeing the building program, Fernandez-Moran joined a Venezuelan delegation (that included Marcel Roche and headed by mathematician Francisco Jose Duarte), to the first United Nations Conference on the Peaceful Uses of Atomic Energy, held in Geneva. This conference was a follow-up to President Eisenhower's speech before the U.N. General Assembly, on December 8, 1953, where in ringing terms he announced his "atoms for peace," and proposed the establishment under the U.N. of an International Atomic Energy Agency, which came into being in 1957. Realizing the potential for nuclear physics, Fernandez-Moran persuaded the Perez Jimenez government in 1957, to invest in an atomic research reactor for his institute. Thus, Venezuela was one of the first countries to accept Eisenhower's atoms for peace offer. However, to some it seemed a bit much for Venezuela to have a nuclear reactor, when it was in its infancy in research.

On **January 23, 1958**, the Perez Jimenez government fell, and as Dr. Fernandez-Moran had been named Minister of Education in the final days of the government, he too had to go into exile. His departure was the U.S.'s gain. He spent four years in Boston, at Massachusetts General Hospital as a biophysicist in neurosurgery where he organized the Mixter Laboratories for Electronic Microscopy, and was a visiting lecturer in biology at MIT, and a research associate in neuropathology at Harvard. In 1962, he accepted a full professorship of biophysics at the University of Chicago.

At Chicago, he created a multi-million dollar laboratory and assembled a staff of scientists and students that pushed high-resolution electron microscopy to its limits. He spent years improving a superfluid helium system and improving the resolving power of the electron microscope. His pioneering studies led to new ways of looking at the brain.

Among Dr. Fernandez-Moran's scientific contributions are two great tools for scientific research: the superconducting electron microscope, and the diamond knife, with an edge so sharp that it can slice through individual cells. He developed the tools to examine "the ultimate structure of life: the diamond knife to pare thin sections of membrane, and an electron microscope chilled by a superfluid helium system to magnify them millions of times. Fernandez-Moran has built a new concept of the way living systems work." [3] With low-temperature ultramicrotome, Fernandez-Moran initiated molecular sectioning of DNA.

He authored several hundred publications, received dozens of awards and honors bestowed on him by many countries and prestigious institutions. Of enormous help to a scientist for research and teaching, Dr. Fernandez-Moran speaks Spanish, English, Swedish, French, and German fluently, plus four other languages. In 1976, Mike McCormack, chairman of a U.S. House of Representatives' Energy Research Development subcommittee, said in introducing Professor Fernandez-Moran prior to his testimony, "he has more advanced degrees, in more outstanding disciplines, then any other witness we have had before this committee." In the many scientific articles published about his work in the United States and in Europe, he is usually described as a "a renaissance man" — biophysicist, physician, neurologist, neuropathologist, radiation authority, inventor of cryogenic electron microscopes, philosopher, former diplomat for

[3] Richard S. Lewis, "Humberto Fernandez-Moran," *Men of Science*, 1972, p. 391

Venezuela, and Principal Investigator in NASA's Apollo Lunar Research Program and Space Shuttle Program.

Dr. Fernandez-Moran has had one overriding passion — for Venezuela — and for educating its youth. For him, America is an indivisible entity, as Simon Bolivar conceived of it, as a Pan American Union. In a speech he gave before the Industrial Research Inc., I-R 100 Awards, in 1968, which was honoring him, Fernandez-Moran ended his talk with a quote from Simon Bolivar, from his Address in Angostura, February 15, 1819:

> My imagination, taking flight to the ages to come, is captured by the vision of future centuries. . . . I seem to see my country at the very heart of the universe . . . I behold her shipping to all corners of the earth the treasures . . . which lie hidden in her mountains. I can see her confiding her precious secrets to the learned men who do not know that her store of knowledge is superior to the wealth with which Nature has prodigally endowed her.

In 1989, Dr. Fernandez-Moran retired from the University of Chicago, and moved to Bern, Switzerland, in ill health. In 1990, he returned to the U.S. to seek treatment for a brain tumor. What irony! One important dream eluded him — a Venezuelan Institute of Technology modeled after the Massachusetts Institute of Technology, with knowledgeable professors capable of teaching in a truly international university. In the United States, as in Europe and elsewhere, Dr. Fernandez-Moran was always known and identified as a **Venezuelan scientist**.

The one institute he had founded in Venezuela, in 1955, was changed after his departure, in 1958. IVNIC was altered from specializing in brain research to become a broader research and training center in science and applied technology, and Dr. Marcel Roche was appointed Director, by the new government junta. The scientists from the Institute of Medical Research, which Dr. Roche had founded, now moved to IVNIC. The new Director recommended that the government create a new institution devoted not only to neurology, but also to physics, chemistry, biology, medicine, mathematics, etc.. Thus, a year after the fall of the Perez Jimenez government, the Government Junta under Edgar Sanabria decreed IVNIC's end, and IVIC's creation, on February 9, 1959. IVIC is where the Petroleum and Petrochemical Center was created in June 1973, which became the core of researchers for **Intevep**.

● ● ●

This is a curious journey — from studies of man's brain, to the depths of the planet that man lives on for the energy man needs. Along the way we meet some remarkable men — some giants! Abraham Lincoln in his famous Springfield Lyceum speech of 1838, said something very apropro to these Venezuelan giants:

Towering genius disdains a beaten path. It seeks regions hitherto unexplored. It sees **no distinction** in adding story to story, upon the monuments of fame erected to the memory of others. It **denies** that it is glory enough to serve under any chief. It **scorns** to tread in the footsteps of **any** predecessor, however illustrious. It thirsts and burns for distinction, and, if possible, it will have it . . . .

Among such men, Lincoln cited Alexander, Caesar, and Napoleon, the three great destroyers of republics, who would destroy if they could not create. Lincoln was speaking of leaders of regimes — for government, as Lincoln and Aristotle saw it, is required not only to overcome the ills of human nature, but to give scope to the good. The problem is that government in infancy brings the best men forward and the best out of these men when governing or experimenting. They are the risk takers. However, once the game is caught, i.e., with attainment, end the pleasures of the chase. This field of glory is harvested. The same can be said about creating research institutes, certainly this was the case in Venezuela. The problem, therefore, is how do you keep, and get, the best men *after* the harvest?

In Venezuela the scientist necessarily becomes involved with politics and with the government! Nowhere is Aristotle's teaching that "man is a rational political animal" more appropriate than in the small scientific community in Venezuela. Their financial support comes from the government, their charters come from the government, all of which makes it important to have friends in high government positions. With the exception of the Roche Foundation, Eugenio Mendoza Foundation, and the Polar Foundation, created in 1977, which grants the Lorenzo Mendoza Fleury prize in basic science with no bureaucratic strings attached, Venezuelans have not established private research funding, which is a common practice in the United States and gives the scientist a modicum of independence. What one government administration has started and supported may become an orphan in the next presidential administration (A.D. or Copei parties).

● ● ●

One foreign oil company, Standard's Creole Petroleum Corporation, did make an enormous contribution in private funding of education and research in Venezuela — prior to nationalization in 1975. Created by the Creole board, in October **1956**, the **Creole Foundation** was the first such organization operated by a U.S. corporation outside the United States. The Foundation's charter provided for Creole funding up to $1,530,000 per year for the first five years. The Foundation began a program for scholarships, subsidized university exchange seminars, set up laboratories at major universities, and awarded a $10,000 prize for the most important scientific achievement in any given year on a Venezuelan subject. It contributed to schools of forestry and soil mechanics, and aided university libraries. A Venezuelan, Alfredo Anzola was President of the Creole Foundation.

The scholarship plan became the Foundation's best known program, for many of its recipients later became prominent in public life and business. Anzola believed that Venezuela needed special expertise in engineering and in the sciences. Most of the grants were for scholarships, with only around 10% going to fellowships for advanced work in foreign universities. But perhaps the greatest payoff were the fellowships, which funded the first 50 outstanding scientists of Venezuela.

Other numerous Creole Foundation activities included: support of a school that taught modern fishing techniques at the La Salle Natural Science Foundation's research station on Margarita Island; and cooperation with the Venezuelan Society for Natural Sciences, in applied biology in the Llanos Study, in new grass varieties and better agricultural techniques. The Creole Foundation's primary contribution was its institution-building effort — acting through other organizations and institutions.

One of the Creole Foundation's most unique gifts in Venezuela was the Jusepin camp that it gave in 1961, to the administration of a new Eastern Venezuela university — Universidad de Oriente. The Jusepin camp consisted of: a variety of large buildings, 660 houses, water, gas, and sanitary facilities. It became the home for schools of petroleum engineering, veterinary science, zoology, geology, engineering, agriculture and mining. Humberto Calderon Berti, who had so much to do with starting and organizing Intevep, was the director of the School of Petroleum Engineering at the Universidad de Oriente, between 1968 and 1970.

Venezuelan Institute of Scientific Research (IVIC) - 1959

After IVNIC there was IVIC. Dr. Fernandez-Moran went into exile in January 1958. **Dr. Marcel Roche** then went to IVNIC, which became IVIC (Instituto Venezolano de Investigaciones Cientificos). Dr. Roche was Director of the Institute from 1958 to 1969, and is responsible for its early growth. In 1969, he was appointed the first President of the newly formed CONICIT, after being the Coordinator of the Commission that studied and advised the Venezuelan Congress on the law that created CONICIT.

Marcel Roche in his book, *My Commitment to Science* (Mi compromiso con la ciencia) published in 1985, states that while he has made some contributions to scientific medicine in his research of endemic goiter and tropical anemias, his commitment has been in helping others, younger than he, to pursue scientific pursuits in order to improve Venezuela and its culture. Toward this end, he has published a great deal on the problem of science in Venezuela. Dr. Roche believes that bridges must be built between scientists and the beneficiaries of science, and this is done by scientific journalists. These scientists must inform while being literate, i.e., they cannot write in scientific jargon, for if they do the public will not read what they write, and the bridge will not be crossed. He hits the target on page 16 of his book when he states that "In the spoken or written word, in order to make a statement one should say the least in stating the most. In English it is called an understatement."

Marcel Roche studied in Europe and in the United States. His secondary education was in France, where he studied the humanities and philosophy. He probably would have dedicated his life to literature, however, with the approaching war in Europe, his father in 1938 sent him to the United States to study. In the U. S., he came under the spell of the objective, precision of scientific method while studying chemistry, physics, and biology in preparing to enter Johns Hopkins School of Medicine. In 1951, he returned to Venezuela, after receiving his M.D. in 1946, followed by internship at Johns Hopkins, residency at Peter Bent Brigham Hospital in Boston, and as researcher and instructor at the Harvard School of Medicine.

Realizing that the relative absence of scientific research in the past was a powerful factor in the country's backwardness, Dr. Roche returned to Caracas to gather men like Dr. Francisco De Venanzi together and formed his private Luis Roche Foundation, the Medical Research Institute (Instituto de Investigaciones Medicas, or IIM), which he headed until he went to IVIC, and took the IIM group with him. Roche explains that Latin America has been a region that has produced primary goods and imported manufactured products. Only since the 1930s has the region commenced to industrialize. The lack of research, until recently, in the oil industry in Venezuela is a shining example in Latin America of the lack of interest in research. Other examples, which Dr. Roche cites, are copper in Chile and tin in Bolivia.

The purpose for the creation of IVIC in 1959, was the desire to contribute in a direct manner to Venezuela's development through its own technology using its own research. Marcel Roche was director of IVIC through two different presidential administrations — both of the Accion Democratica (AD) party — Romulo Betancourt (1959-1964) and Raul Leoni (1964-1969). Slowly a considerable degree of confidence and credibility developed regarding IVIC's capability and recommendations.

President Rafael Caldera (1969-1974), founder of the COPEI party, made periodic visits to IVIC's headquarters for an exchange of ideas with Dr. Raimundo Villegas and his staff. Under President Caldera, the Institute grew even more, adding new centers to IVIC: the Technological Center; the Petroleum and Petrochemical Center; the Center for Advanced Studies; the Latin American Biology Center; and the start of the process to create the International Ecology Center. From several of these centers new scientific institutes were later created, like Intevep, IDEA (International Institute of Advanced Studies, in 1979), and the Institute for Engineering. And the Center for Advanced Studies granted the *first* master and doctorate degrees in science, in Venezuela.

In 1969, President Caldera appointed **Raimundo Villegas, M.D.**, a graduate of the Central University of Venezuela, with postdoctoral training at Vanderbilt University, Harvard, and the Marine Biological Laboratory at Woods Hole, to become the new Director of IVIC. Dr. Villegas is another example of a physician becoming a distinguished scientist, and administrator of IVIC. But Dr. Villegas is unique in one respect. His wife Gloria Mercader de Villegas, M.D., is also a medical doctor, who also graduated from the Central University of Venezuela and did her postdoctoral training in Boston, and was Venezuela's leading female medical researcher at IVIC. Dr. Gloria Villegas was hired, along with her husband, by Dr. Marcel Roche when he went to IVNIC, in 1958. Both Doctors Villegas formed part of a team that was researching the nervous system. At IVIC, Raimundo Villegas founded the department of biophysics and later headed the Center of Biophysics and Biochemistry, until his appointment as Director of IVIC.

Dr. Villegas was director at IVIC between 1969 and 1974, which was the previously mentioned growth period under President Caldera. For Intevep, this was a basic formative stage, for not only was the Petroleum and Petrochemical Center created that would later form the core of researchers at Intevep, the Center for Advanced Studies would be a source of future researchers.

With the new administration of Carlos Andres Perez (1974-1979), Dr. Villegas was replaced at IVIC in 1974, by **Luis Carbonell**, a pathologist, who in 1984 became Minister of State (once more following Villegas). As stated earlier, scientists in Venezuela need friends in high government positions because of their institute's dependence on public funding. Professor Villegas returned to appointed office as Minister of State for Science and Technology in 1979, under President Luis Herrera Campins (1979-1984). The priorities that the new Minister established were: 1) to study the most convenient mechanism to coordinate and develop research institutions at the top level, without disturbing their respective formal links with their *corresponding ministries*, 2) to encourage research in the provinces, 3) to develop both high-quality basic research and applied research in priority areas, and 4) to create mechanisms for international scientific cooperation, and reinforce those that already exist. [4]

At the same time that Dr. Villegas was Minister of State he was also President of IDEA (Advanced Studies), which he helped to found. Presently, Professor Villegas continues his research at IDEA, working with his wife, Gloria, on the excitable membrane of the nerve. He is Director of the Biosciences Unit, and continues to write and publish and promote scientific research in Latin America. IDEA was organized as a joint foundation with state and private participation — and open to cooperation by international organizations. Its purpose was top-level scientific education and research through international workshops and intensive training courses. Since its creation, IDEA has been the headquarters of several international scientific organizations, e.g., the Latin American Academy of Sciences, and the Simon Bolivar International Center for Scientific Cooperation created by a UNESCO - Venezuela Agreement.

IVIC was officially created February 9, 1959, by decree No. 551, under the Government Junta headed by Edgar Sanabria. It is an autonomous institute, inscribed under the Ministry of Health and Social Welfare, whose activities are concentrated on:

● Basic and applied research,
● Graduate education for Masters and Doctorate degrees,
● Scientific and technical library center — the Marcel Roche Library (now around 60,000 volumes, with 4,000 subscriptions to scientific and technical journals, making it the largest in Venezuela). Virginia Betancourt Valverde, the Director of the National System of Libraries, and the daughter of Romulo Betancourt, has stated that the IVIC library founded by Dr. Fernandez-Moran is the best scientific library in Latin America.
● Adviser to the National Executive on science and technology,
● Consulting work and assistance to related research elsewhere.

The Institute has 10 centers, or departments, with 58 laboratories. The Centers are: Biophysics and Biochemical; Chemistry; Ecology and Environmental Science; Engineering; Experimental Medicine;

---

[4] Raimundo Villegas, "Scientific Advising to the President of Venezuela," *Worldwide Science and Technology*, Advice to the Highest Levels of Governments, W. T. Golden, Ed. (New York: Pergamon Press, 1990)

Microbiology and Cellular Biology; Physics; and the Departments of: Anthropology; Mathematics; and, Studies in Science. In 1990, IVIC had 104 researchers, with several hundred in other research categories, like: professional associates, post doctoral contractors, visiting researchers, etc. Of the 137 graduate students studying at IVIC, 30 were IVIC employees.

IVIC scholarship holders returned to Venezuela, and some started new electronic and nuclear service companies. Most important, from IVIC were born other research institutes!

IVIC is funded by the Venezuelan Government, by contract work, and by patents. In 1988, Dr. Horacio Vanegas became the Director of IVIC, replacing Dr. Boris Drujan. (The first Director was Roche, followed by Villegas, Carbonell, Drujan, and Vanegas.) Unfortunately, in April 1992, Dr. Vanegas and his Board (including Dr. Barroeta of Intevep, and Dr. Carbonell) resigned over an illegal strike by a few members of the labor union (SEPIVIC) at IVIC, regarding a salary and collective contract dispute. The strike caused considerable damage to IVIC. A new Director and Board was appointed by the Perez Government, only to have them resign within days.

National Science and Technology Research Council (CONICIT) - 1969

T he Consejo Nacional de Investigaciones Cientificas y Tecnologicas, known as CONICIT, was created by Congress in 1968, under the Raul Leoni administration (1964-1969). In June 1969, after a long consultation process, CONICIT started to function under the Rafael Caldera administration (1969-1974).

In 1962, a commission was set up to prepare studies for the law necessary to create CONICIT. Marcel Roche was the Coordinator of the Commission, and the **first President** of CONICIT in 1969 — just as he had been of the Roche Foundation, of IVIC, of the Petroleum Working Group, and of the Petroleum and Petrochemical Research Commission to identify research needs in the oil industry and create Invepet/Intevep. It is as clear as the sun that comes up in the morning that Marcel Roche has been a tour de force in Venezuela!

CONICIT is an autonomous institute that depends on the Venezuelan Presidency through CORDIPLAN (the President's Planning and Coordination Central Office). Those that studied and proposed CONICIT were not only scientists but members of the industrial sector. CONICIT was set up with a Council of 21 representatives from different institutions, who meet once a week. It was designed as the national government's advisory agency in the area of science and technology. Its task was to promote scientific and technological research, by allocating funds to finance postgraduate studies and research activities. For the fist time, under President Caldera, on the advice of the Council, a chapter on science and technology was included in a national development plan.

Under President Jaime Lusinchi (1984-1989), of the Accion Democratica party, **Dr. Luis Carbonell** was named Minister of State for Science and Technology **and** President of CONICIT! The new post received both a larger staff and budget. The political nature of the Minister of State cannot help but influence the scientific and technical decisions made by the President of CONICIT. However, on the positive side for CONICIT, it now has a voice in the Cabinet.

Congress also changed the legal status of foundations that had received significant contributions from the Government when they were created. They would now be considered State foundations — and not so autonomous! The President could now freely appoint and remove the officers, and most of the members of their councils had to be appointed by the government. Curiously, the foundations created during the Herrera Campins administration (from the other political party, COPEI) were the ones mainly affected by the new law.

Invepet - 1974-1975

T he creation of Invepet by presidential decree in August 1973, as the Foundation for Research in Hydrocarbons and Petrochemicals **(Fundacion para la Investigacion en Hidrocarburos y Petroquimica)** was part of the process that Marcel Roche's group at CONICIT commenced, in 1970. Their principal accomplishments were: the report they produced on technology transfer, known as the *Diagnostico Sobre Transferencia Tecnologica de la Industria Petrolera* (Diagnosis of the

Transfer of Technology in the Petroleum Industry); the Master Plans; and the feasibility studies.

Most of the funding for this effort was through **FONINVES**, established February 27, 1974, by decree of President Rafael Caldera, to fund research in hydrocarbons and train personnel for the oil and petrochemical industry. The name Foninves stood for a very long title, which was shortened to Fondo de Investigacion (Fund for Research), or FONINVES. The Bs.1,143,503,500 appropriated by the government for Foninves was essential for the launching of Invepet and modern research in the oil industry in Venezuela. This fund paid the salaries at Invepet and the IVIC petroleum group, and purchased lab equipment for research at the universities.

The Fund was placed under the Ministry of Mines and Hydrocarbons, and administered by an ad-hoc Council, whose nine members represented: the Ministry of Mines, the national oil company (CVP, which comprised 5% of the oil industry), CONICIT, Ministry of Education (through the National Council of Universities), CORDIPLAN, FEDEPETROL (the union of oil workers), the College of Engineers of Venezuela, IVIC, and the Petrochemical Institute. Four members of this Council would later work at Intevep: Jose Martorano Batisti, President of the Council, (representing the Ministry of Mines), Miguel Layrisse (CONICIT), Nestor Barroeta (IVIC), and Rolf Becker (Petrochemicals-IVP).

In 1983, with the creation of CEPET (PDVSA's management and training center) the scholarship program and activities of Foninves were absorbed by CEPET. One of the worthy programs that Foninves sponsored was the publication of scientific books on the industry. Most noteworthy is *Geologia de Venezuela y de sus Cuencas Petroliferas* (Geology of Venezuela and its Petroleum Basins) in two volumes, in 1980. CEPET is continuing this practice and in 1989, published *La Industria Venezolana de los Hidrocarburos* (The Venezuelan Industry of Hydrocarbons), also in two volumes.

The **Diagnosis** is 239 pages of carefully compiled information about the transfer of technology in the oil industry in Venezuela. The opening sentence states the concern in Venezuela: "The new structure of a nationalized petroleum industry will change the links that the concessionaires maintain with their respective parent companies." The Venezuelan oil industry did not want to be cut off from the international oil industry and technical developments, the way Mexico had been after 1938. Therefore, the first order of business was to assess what technology was developed in

Venezuela, and where they could purchase needed technology. They divided the task between four groups to study: **exploration, production, refining, and computation/computer systems.**

The study (diagnosis) found that the concessionaires varied in composition and function. Some depended on local resources, whereas others depended exclusively on their parent companies. It became clear that an inventory of Venezuelan talent and experience was needed, in order to manage a nationalized petroleum industry. Between 1960 and 1975, the number of Venezuelans with expertise in different aspects of technology had increased. In the **exploration area**, service companies were more important than the *casas matrices* (parent companies). In the **production area**, there was transfer of technology between the *casas matrices* and service companies. However, in **refining**, the casa matrices were much more important. The refining section of the diagnosis took up half of the study. For the diagnosis, the Invepet oilmen also made an evaluation of the research labs of the parent companies, and found that some (Shell and Exxon) fully supported these research centers. If Venezuela was to elevate research to a comparable level and fund on this basis, and on the basis of its oil production, it would need 1,000 professionals and Bs.350 million annually. (refer to end of Diagnosis section)

Up until 1975, Venezuelans had timidly participated in developing new technology because it was so easy to purchase abroad. The diagnosis points out - structural, nechanical, electrical, metallurgical and corrosion engineering - as examples of little used areas domestically. Nor were the services and help of university laboratories, or scientific institution like IVIC, used by the oil industry.

When the oil industry started, they depended on their own resources. However, as the industry grew an infra-structure developed, i.e., service companies, to compliment the companies' operations. In 1975, **45%** of the costs of the Venezuelan oil industry went to purchase these services. The types of services available in Venezuela were: 1) specialized services requiring a high degree of technology, which requires ongoing research, e.g., electric logging, and seismic studies; 2) drilling, workovers, well completions and stimulation; 3) supply of tools and equipment; and 4) general engineering services.

Service companies performed a vital function as a link between the oil companies and the rest of the industry, and one can also add, with the rest of the country! Seldom noted, but very important: when nationalization of the oil industry in Venezuela occurred in 1975, **45%** of the industry was **not nationalized**, i.e., the service companies!!

The first chapter of the Diagnosis was on **exploration**. Exploration had decreased a great deal in the preceding 15 years, *because* there were no new concessions granted after Romulo Betancourt became President in 1959. (This last point is not pointed out in the Diagnosis.) In the 1950s, 150 wildcat wells were drilled per year. Ten years later, only 40 wells per year were drilled. In the 1950s, the industry added 700 million barrels per year in oil reserves. Ten years later, only 50 million barrels per year of reserves were added. Venezuela was producing its reserves without replacing them. All of this brought a decline of personnel in the industry! In 1955, about 800 professionals in exploration were employed in the oil industry, but by the end of 1974, there were only 44 professionals in exploration. Many of these explorationists had been assigned other work, but would be available once exploration resumed in Venezuela.

Areas where exploration was particularly needed: 1) Continental offshore; 2) Orinoco Delta; 3) Deep drilling in Lake Maracaibo; and 4) Orinoco Oil Belt.

They listed the different scientific professions necessary to carry out the exploration and found that the needed personnel were in Venezuela, e.g., geophysicists, geologists, paleontologists, oceanographers, etc.. They would need the help of the foreign oil companies to select the right technology for the different exploratory work, and Invepet should be involved, so that it could begin to learn this operation. Laboratories for geological work were essential, preferably near exploration work, with a centralized research geophysical data center to collect field information. To this end, a geology laboratory was recommended for Invepet.

Production, the second chapter in the Diagnosis, was viewed as the most important area, because it had the largest number of employees and budget dedicated to the maintenance of 3 million b/d. The parent companies, as well as domestic service companies, supplied technology to this operation. Drilling, in particular, was supplied by service companies, while transportation was mainly dependent on the concessionaires. The major oil companies in the previous 15 years had used Venezuelan engineering service companies, however, the smaller companies used their parent company.

The study pointed out that as production declined in the old oil fields, Venezuela would need to use enhanced oil recovery (EOR) and would need more advanced technology to maintain production. Not only was EOR technology needed, technology was needed to develop new areas in the Orinoco Oil Belt and the Offshore Continental Shelf.

There were three methods of technology transfer between the parent companies and their Venezuelan affiliates: training; information and general consulting; and technical and research advise. The last one was the most important. The Venezuelans needed to find a means of maintaining technical advice and the availability to advances in research. (One of the members of this Invepet diagnosis group was Nelson Vasquez of Shell, who one day would be president of Intevep.)

Refining was the third and longest chapter of the Diagnosis, for it was the operation that badly needed upgrading. The last major refining project in Venezuela was at Amuay (Creole), in 1967-68. The refining study was put together with the assistance of the General Managers of the four large refineries, who were Venezuelan. The General Manager of Amuay, Venezuela's largest refinery and since 1982 the largest in the world (replacing Amerada Hess in the Virgin Islands), was Renato Urdaneta, who would later become President of Pequiven, of Meneven, of Lagoven, and now is heading the Cristobal Colon LNG project. Approximately 98% of the personnel in the refining operation was Venezuelan. However, there was concern over the exodus of personnel in this operation. The reasons for the departure of refining personnel were: the increased industrialization in Venezuela, therefore, competition for these trained men; and secondly, because of approaching nationalization some of the more educated and mobile, who were worried about working for a state company, were leaving.

In Venezuela, the pattern of refineries was relatively simple. Amuay's 670,000 b/d distillation capacity had no catalytic cracking or alkylation capacity. Venezuela then had 12 refineries with a total distillation capacity of 1.4 million b/d. (Obviously, Amuay represented nearly half of the total capacity.) Because of this lack of upgrading, Venezuela could not easily produce the more expensive and lighter, white products, like gasoline and distillates, which are in greater demand. Venezuela was a big producer of residual fuel oil, i.e., the bottom of the barrel.

Venezuela urgently needed to convert and upgrade its large refineries so that it could refine not only lighter products to sell domestically, but because the demand for residual oil in the United States was declining and it was losing its market. **And**, it needed to be able to refine its heavier crudes, like Boscan, and the future extra-heavy oil production from the Orinoco Oil Belt. Venezuela was refining its more valuable light and medium crudes, but was unable to refine its heavy crudes, which made up the largest part of its proven reserves. It is better to export your light crudes because you get a higher price for those crudes, and in turn refine your heavy crudes and export their products. But conversion and upgrading to process heavy crudes is very expensive, and the foreign concessionaires did not want to make these large investments abroad. They were in the business of producing oil overseas to supply their refineries in the United States and Europe.

Finally, **computer systems**, in the fourth chapter of the Diagnosis, was found to be the area in which the concessionaires were self sufficient, for there was little or no technology transfer. Computer programs were still new to the oil industry. The development of new systems seemed ideal for Invepet to work with the foreign companies. The large concessionaires were then using the MARK-IV system, however, additions to the system were constantly needed and the Venezuelan industry would have to purchase these additions.

The dissemination of information via bulletins, special publications, or joint projects, reports on equipment failures, etc., were also recognized as important, in this group's study. They recommended that as a first step Invepet establish a bi-monthly technical bulletin for computation. The next step was to train personnel in systems and programming.

The Diagnosis is a very good study, however, it has several inconsistencies between the executive summary and the different chapters. For example, on page 4 of the summary, it says that "around 1,000 professionals and Bs.350 million annually will be needed for research and development of the oil industry." However, on page 96 in the Production chapter, it states that "around 1,000 professionals and an annual budget of approximately Bs.500 million dedicated to research and technology" would be necessary to maintain the current production levels. Then there was the difference between the Venezuelan personnel working in the refineries. The Refining chapter on page 103 listed the total Venezuelans at approximately 98.9%, and the technical Venezuelans at 99.4%, while the summary on page 18 had 97.5% and 90% respectively, as working in the refineries. Were these merely uncaught typos or did the author of the summary decide to make changes?

The Diagnosis was sent to Valentin Hernandez, Minister of Mines and Hydrocarbons, by Humberto Calderon Berti, President of Invepet, on April 22, 1975. The 40 professionals in the four working groups had first been assembled in November 1974. It was a remarkable feat because nearly all members had full time positions in the oil companies or at the Ministry.

This important Invepet study had a driving force behind it — the President of Invepet: **Humberto Calderon Berti**. President Calderon Berti stated in an interview for this book that Intevep is an exceptional case in a developing country because the founders were not scientists but great managers. "The result is permanency." There was method to the founding. This young geologist, with a Masters in petroleum engineering from the University of Tulsa, was on a very fast track. He was only 33 years old in 1974, when he became President of Invepet, **and** 38 when he became Minister of Energy and Mines.

After serving as director of the School of Petroleum Engineering at the Universidad de Oriente (East) for two years, he worked in the Ministry of Mines and Hydrocarbons, was appointed to the Board of Corporacion Venezolana del Petroleo, and was Director of Oil Reversion in the Ministry of Mines. It was during his work on reversion of the oil industry that he was also president of Invepet.

Calderon Berti went on to be the CEO and Vice-President of Intevep, until he was appointed Minister of Energy and Mines (name changed in 1977, and now known as MEM, for Ministerio de Energia y Minas) between 1979-1983, under President Herrera Campins (COPEI). While he was Minister, Calderon was elected President of OPEC, 1979-1980. Before President Herrera ended his term, he appointed Calderon Berti, President of Petroleos de Venezuela. This did not sit well in the oil industry, or with the other political party (AD) that won the next election. The new President of Venezuela, Jaime Lusinchi, replaced Calderon Berti with Brigido Natera, the first man from the oil industry to be appointed President of PDVSA. (Before Calderon Berti's appointment in 1983, General Rafael Alfonzo Ravard had been the first and only president of PDVSA. Ironically, it was the General who insisted that Calderon Berti not be given the title of President of Intevep in 1976, even though he was in charge and CEO of the Institute he launched.)

It was fortunate that Calderon Berti carried considerable political clout in the formative years of Invepet and Intevep — for it was his ability to ramrod, move, and keep the institute growing that is the reason that Venezuela has Intevep, today. He had help from friends: like Evanan Romero, also with a Masters in petroleum engineering from the University of Tulsa and whose Stanford University connection (where he studied for a doctorate) brought in Dr. Stewart Blake to give them the needed guidance; Valentin Hernandez, Minister of Mines, who came through with needed support and funds at a critical time; and Winston Peraza, a chemical engineer from the petrochemical industry. And finally, he was helped by President Carlos Andres Perez, who made the decision to give Invepet to the newly created Petroleos de Venezuela.

As Director of Reversion, Calderon Berti received the high and mighty of the oil industry. Men like Alberto Quiros of Shell/Maraven, and Guillermo Rodriguez Eraso of Creole/Lagoven, and Bernardo Diaz of Mene Grande/Meneven were forced to listen to him talk about Invepet, and give their assistance. It was Minister Valentin Hernandez (now deceased) who went to Miraflores (the Presidential palace) at the end of December 1975, and signed the decree (which Calderon Berti, Evanan Romero, and Winston Peraza had written), to include Invepet in the nationalization of the oil industry and thus created **Intevep**, which was named by Carlos Andres Perez. Up till then, Invepet was "a center of research without researchers." (Winston Peraza)

With time, one can observe that the change in name was more significant than first imagined. The August 29, 1973, Decree 1385, signed by President Rafael Caldera, Enrique Perez Olivares, Minister of Education, and Hugo Perez La Salvia, Minister of Mines and Hydrocarbons, gave Invepet the name and the purpose to *Investigate* (research) Hydrocarbons and Petrochemicals. And it was called a *foundation* in Article 1, where it said it was to promote scientific research and technology.

Note that the Education Minister signed the decree, and that research (or investigate) was in the name of this institute, which was called a foundation. However, when Carlos Andres Perez changed the name of Invepet to Intevep, the descriptive words also changed — because the purpose had changed. Foundation was replaced with Institute, and Research was replaced with Technology. To anyone involved with basic research, this had to be worrisome. In the last three chapters we will observe the significance of the name change.

The connecting thread to research in Venezuela has *always been* politics! Invepet was installed on **February 7, 1974**, a month *before* Carlos Andres Perez (AD) was inaugurated as President. Humberto Calderon Berti (of COPEI), who was already Director of Oil Reversion in the Ministry, was thus installed as President of Invepet. In August the following year, the oil industry was nationalized. And when Calderon Berti, along with Evanan Romero and Winston Peraza, went to see General Alfonzo Ravard and the new PDVSA Board in December 1975, to present their proposal for Invepet to become PDVSA's research institute, the General listened politely, but did not appear interested in acquiring Invepet. Calderon Berti in an interview with the author in November 1989, said that the General made the three of them feel like school boys with school books under their arms.

A dinner speech on the "Organization of PDVSA," which the General gave on November 25, 1975, before the Venezuelan Press Club, supported the impression that a research institute for PDVSA was not on the General's agenda. He spoke of the need to maintain the transfer of foreign technology, and the need for a Center of Technology Development to act as a *vehicle* for technology transfer. There was no hint or suggestion that research for the oil industry might be done in Venezuela under PDVSA's mantle. As Calderon Berti told the author, "We were the unwanted child that the General was forced to accept when President Perez presented Invepet to PDVSA in January 1976."

Intevep - 1976

istory has a way of being written quite differently than the way it was forecast. And even after time passes, the cause-effect of some men's actions are not clearly understood. Had the General — a proud man, who was a graduate of the Ecole Superieur du Guerre in France, with a civil engineering degree from the Massachusetts Institute of Technology, and with 14 years experience as president of the Guayana Development Corporation (CVG) — had he not been so obvious about this unwanted son, Intevep, the ongoing animus relationship between the Minister of Energy and the President of PDVSA might not have been etched in stone. The General was a reasonable political choice for the first President of Petroleos de Venezuela, **and** Humberto Calderon Berti was the obvious choice as the first President of Intevep. As we say in the U.S. venacular, "Humberto got his licks in, later, when he was Minister."

When Calderon Berti became Minister of Energy in 1979, the General was re-appointed President of PDVSA. However, at the August shareholders (represented by 100 shares in the name of the Republic of Venezuela, whose voting representative is the Minister of Energy) meeting with PDVSA and its affiliates, the new Minister **changed the bylaws.** Board members would have a tenure of 2 years instead of 4 years, and the Board would have two vice-presidents instead of one, **and** the shareholders (the Minister) would have the authority to assign the areas of managerial responsibilities to all members of the Board, **and** the shareholders **would approve or disapprove the budgets of PDVSA.** The young Minister changed the oil industry overnight!! The General had cost the industry dearly. There no longer was to be freedom **from** political interference and **for** professional management practices. (The Statutes that PDVSA now operates under were signed by President Jaime Lusinchi, Septermber 24, 1985, and are basically the same as Calderon Berti's, except, e.g., there are now 3,280 shares, each worth Bs. 25 million.)

While Calderon Berti was Vice-President of Intevep and getting it launched, he would often have to by-pass the General and go directly to Minister Valentin Hernandez for help. The General did not want to authorize the purchase of Villa Pignatelli for the institute. He said there was no money for this purchase. But nothing was going to stop this young petroleum engineer from building his research center. And build it he did!

Calderon won the site he selected in Los Teques, over strong opposition from those who wanted Intevep to be located in Western Venezuela in the oil producing state of Zulia. He also sought the best advice — from a recognized authority on technical research and development programs, Dr. Stewart Blake from Stanford; and the well known California architectural firm W. L. Pereira Associates — to work on Invepet/Intevep's Master Plan. And he gathered a vigorous and dedicated team to commence the process of establishing oil research in Venezuela, so that Venezuela would not always depend on expensive technical assistance (service) contracts, known as CATs in Venezuela, with former concessionaires.

The Intevep ship was on full throttle until Calderon Berti left, in 1979, after Luis Herrera Campins, who was inaugurated President of Venezuela, on March 12, 1979, appointed his friend Minister of Energy and Mines, where he remained for four and a half years. After Calderon left Intevep, it became a commercial enterprise, modeled like an oil company, instead of a research institute. With so much controversy over its creation, the first mission of Intevep was to win credibility. Therefore, after the physical planning stage, the first task was service work! Research would come later.

Unfortunately, in 1983, there was an overall freeze on personnel in the industry, a result of the Venezuelan financial crisis brought on by the prolific spending of the Perez government in the 1970s and the inability of the Herrera government to halt the growing Venezuelan foreign debt, which caused enormous capital flight that cut deeply into Venezuela's international reserves, at a time when the world price of oil was declining. This financial crisis and freeze on hiring personnel coincided with Calderon Berti's departure from power, when Jaime Lusinchi (AD) became President of Venezuela, in early February 1984.

After Calderon Berti's departure from Intevep in 1979, the institute would have a series of oilmen as president, and it would be run like an oil company. This will be covered in Chapter IV. The following chapter, Chapter III, is a brief history of the Venezuelan oil industry, to acquaint the reader with the industry that Intevep is now part of, as well as highlight the unique venture that the U.S. companies and Shell were engaged in with the Venezuelans for 60 years.

But first a few concluding points on the giants who clashed over the creation of Intevep and how **this clash affected the whole oil industry!** The "politization" of the oil industry that Calderon Berti carried out during his tenure as Minister was only occasionally resisted by the General. With a shortened tenure of two years and wishing to keep his job, the General offered little defense when the Minister attempted inroads into the oil industry.

The months of August turned out to be especially crucial in Minister Calderon's gaining control of Petroleos de Venezuela. On August 26, 1981, Minister Calderon suddenly announced to the press that the main offices of one of the four oil operating companies, Meneven, would be moving from Caracas, to Puerto La Cruz, and that Pequiven (petrochemical) would move from Caracas to Maracaibo. Caracas is the largest city, it is the capital, and most important, it is the center of power in the country. There was no analysis or feasibility study made in the Ministry or PDVSA, for such a momentous move of personnel. But of greater concern, it appeared that the decision making process had moved from PDVSA to the Ministry! The only significant reaction within the industry came from Gustavo Coronel, Vice-President of Meneven, in the form of a letter to General Alfonzo, objecting to the decision. Coronel was dismissed! (Ironically, the move was no longer pertinent after May 1986, when Meneven was integrated into Corpoven.)

When the new PDVSA Board was announced, the first week of September 1981, the General was retained for two more years, but the able Hugo Finol (formerly from Shell) was removed, and replaced with two of the Minister's friends. Nelson Vasquez, an experienced engineer, who had replaced Calderon at Intevep, now was appointed to the PDVSA Board. The perception that the General was reappointed until Calderon was ready to take the job himself, was confirmed in 1982, when Calderon announced that he would be a candidate in August 1983.

On August 31, 1983, President Herrera appointed Calderon to be President of PDVSA. Calderon Berti was only president of PDVSA for five months. Jaime Lusinchi became President of Venezuela on February 6, 1984, and Calderon Berti was replaced on February 8, by Brigido Natera. A reasonable question that comes to mind: Why would anyone want to diminish the power of the office that one was planning on occupying?

During the period that Calderon Berti was Minister of Energy there were some very interesting news **headlines**. Some historical dates and events to remember:

● In May 1979, Intevep became a mercantile society, owned by PDVSA.
● In August 1980, the San Jose Accord was signed by Venezuela and Mexico, to supply oil on advantageous terms to Central America and Caribbean countries.
● In mid-December 1980, there was an OPEC Meeting in Bali, Indonesia, Calderon Berti presiding as OPEC President, where there was an empty chair with a picture of the Iranian oil minister, Ali Akbar Moinfar, who had been taken prisoner by the Iraqis. It was the first time since OPEC was formed in September 1960, that two members were at war destroying each other's refineries, pipelines, and harbour installations. The 20 year anniversary of OPEC was not celebrated in Baghdad as planned (nor the 30th anniversary in 1990, as this time Iraq was occupying Kuwait, another

founding member of OPEC).

● OPEC's power to control oil prices ended, because of: widespread recessions; large oil inventory levels; the removal of price controls in the United States increased production, which caused U.S. oil imports to drop; the decline of long-term oil contracts, and the increase in spot market supplies; all of which caused the Saudis to keep cutting production; until finally, on **March 19, 1982**, OPEC for the first time set a limit on its total crude output and allocated individual production shares! And Venezuela was forced to reduce its oil production in order to conform with its new OPEC **quota.**

● By the end of February 1982, Venezuela was in a deep economic crisis, as the world price of oil continued to decline. The oil industry could see the crisis coming, the Minister could not. The Herrera government's principal concern at the time was in renegotiating the growing foreign debt, which they had inherited from the previous government of Carlos Andres Perez, and which they were increasing. On **October 28, 1982**, the ax fell on Petroleos de Venezuela, when the government transferred PDVSA's foreign dollar accounts ($6 billion) to the Central Bank. In effect, it was the takeover of the oil industry.

● The date remembered by all Venezuelans, is **February 18, 1983,** when the Herrera government ended the fixed exchange rate system of the bolivar, and inflation took off! This action followed a flight of capital (fearing devaluation), which was exacerbated after the government announced it was taking over PDVSA's foreign reserves.

● And just before Calderon left the Ministry in August, to become President of Petroleos de Venezuela, there was the scandal of the "petro spies," the oil traders selling information on oil prices.

These are a few of Venezuela's headlines during 1979-1983, which affected the oil industry when Calderon was Minister.

As for the giants, Lincoln said it in 1838: "Towering genius disdains a beaten path. It seeks regions hitherto unexplored." Such a man is Humberto Calderon Berti. And, where Intevep is concerned, there were a number of giants breaking ground with the help of many other men — so that each could end the chase and harvest the glory. ●

THE ORIGINS OF INTEVEP, S. A.

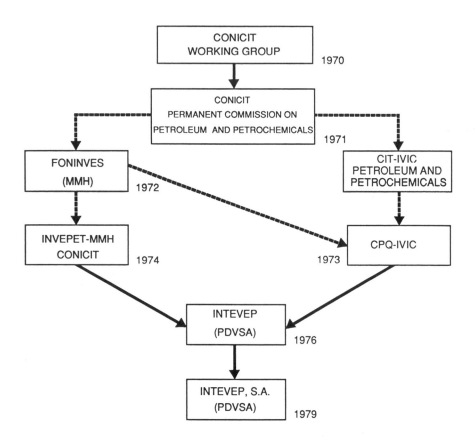

CHAPTER III

BRIEF HISTORY OF VENEZUELA'S BLACK GOLD

E arly in the twentieth century, foreigners arrived in Venezuela to develop Venezuela's greatest natural resource - petroleum. First, the Dutch and English, i.e., Royal Dutch/Shell, arrived and brought in the first commercial oil well, Zumaque I, in the Mene Grande field on the eastern shore of Lake Maracaibo, in 1914. After 1922, waves of US-Americans arrived. **However**, the first oil company in Venezuela was Venezuelan. Named La Petrolia, it was organized in **1878**, in the Andean state of Tachira, and continued in operation until 1934.

In 1922, Shell Oil's well, Los Barrosos No. 2, on the northeastern shore of Lake Maracaibo, blew for 10 days at an estimated 100,000 b/d, and drew the attention of the world to Venezuela as a potentially important source of oil. It marked the beginning of enormous petroleum activity in

Venezuela, and brought in the U.S. oil companies. By 1928, Venezuela was the second largest producer in the world after the United States, with 289,000 b/d, and was the largest exporter, until 1970. (Venezuela was replaced as the world's second largest oil producer in 1961, by the Soviet Union.) Venezuela also had the *world's first super-giant field*—the **Bolivar Coastal Fields**, with proven reserves of 32.2 billion barrels. Lagunillas (1926) has already produced 11 billion barrels.

It was General Juan Vicente Gomez, "El Benemerito," ruler of Venezuela between 1908 and 1935 (when he died), who pushed the development of the petroleum industry in Venezuela. The discovery of oil in Venezuela dates back to the Spanish conquistadores, who mentioned the oil seeps in their records of Lake Maracaibo. Some Spanish historians called the black viscous liquid "stercus demonis," or devil's dung, while others referred to it as "petrolio" or "asfalto." It was used by the Indians to caulk their canoes and for medicinal purposes (to cover their wounds).

And so the Spanish, Gonzalo Fernandez de Oviedo y Valdes, in 1539, shipped a barrel of oil back to Spain, for medicinal purposes. This was the **first** known export of Venezuela's oil across the Atlantic! and it was exported to the Queen for medicinal purposes. It came from Cubagua, a small island south of the large Venezuelan Island of Margarita. For the first century or two, following the discovery of Lake Maracaibo in 1499, by Alonso de Ojeda, it was gold, silver and precious stones that lured the Europeans to explore Venezuela.

Except for English and French pirates, who utilized the oil seeps in the Maracaibo Basin to caulk their ships during the seventeenth century, there was scant interest or knowledge of Venezuela's greatest resource. Alexander von Humboldt, who traveled across Venezuela in the early 1800s, produced the first scientific report on the geology of Venezuela, including the deposits of asphalt from Trinidad to Maracaibo.

After Simon Bolivar was able to liberate Venezuela from Spain, he ratified, in 1829, King Carlos III's Mineral Ordinances of 1784. Bolivar, thereby, transferred to the new Venezuelan Republic the mineral rights formerly possessed by the Spanish Crown. There are no private mineral rights in Venezuela, or any Latin American country - a result of the colonial Law of the Indies (1526, 1559, 1584, 1602, 1680, 1783, and 1784). In 1832, the Venezuelan Congress ratified Bolivar's decree on national ownership of "mines of all kinds." And the Mining Law of 1918 declared that the granting of a concession does **not confer ownership of the deposit,** only the right to exploit the substance! The duration of a concession was set at 30 years. You do not own the oil until you produce it. This is quite different from the tradition of private mineral rights in the U.S., and therefore, is not generally understood in the United States.

In Maracaibo, the principal concern was the lack of drinking water during the dry season, between December and May. As the city grew, the Lake became contaminated by the filth of the city, and the gradual encroachment of salt water from the sea. By 1900, Maracaibo had an incandescent lighting system, but no water system. A private company in Maracaibo contracted a U.S. water well expert in 1897, to study Maracaibo's water problem. After making some test holes, the U.S. expert told the company's directors: "Water can be obtained, but with a great deal of difficulty. I am sorry to have to inform you that what abounds here under the earth is oil."[1]

Up until 1904, the right of exploitation was granted only after discovery, which meant the discoverer had to present a bottled sample to the public official indicated by law before being granted title. But who would drill an expensive well without title to the land? Only those who had oil seeps applied as claimants. President Cipriano Castro, therefore, issued a decree in 1904, that made the exploitation of hydrocarbons possible under special contracts. Concessions were now possible.

A number of contracts were signed with Venezuelan citizens, and several special contracts for the exploitation of **asphalt** were signed with foreign companies. These were the first foreign companies to enter Venezuela to develop petroleum. The first development occurred in small deposits of asphalt in eastern Venezuela, near the **Gulf of Paria.** One group (E. Stanley Simmons) from the United States obtained the rights of Pedro Guzman of Maracaibo to the Inciarte Mine, an asphalt deposit west of Maracaibo. This operation was successful until the State of Zulia seized it and tried to run it.

The big player, however, was the New York & Bermudez Company, a subsidiary of General Asphalt, which signed a contract for 11,000 acres in the Laguna Guanoco, near the Gulf of Paria in eastern Venezuela. This concession had first belonged to H.R. Hamilton, and the Bermudez Company acquired the concession in 1886, but did not begin exploitation of the asphalt, until 1901. The Bermudez Company not only produced asphalt, it drilled for oil to a depth of over 600 feet in 1912, and discovered

---

[1] John Lavin, *A Halo for Gomez,* (New York: Pageant Press, 1954) p. 282

heavy oil. In 1913, with the completion of well Bababui-1, the Guanoco field, in the Maturin Basin, was discovered. The Guanoco asphalt lake is the largest known asphalt deposit in the world. However, there has been no production at Guanoco since the 1930s. The primary source for asphalt now is the vacuum distillation of crude oil in the refinery, however, only a few crude oils can be used for manufacturing asphalt.

Thus, asphalt was the first exploitation done by foreign companies, **before** oil was produced by foreigners. And asphalt produced in Venezuela was used to pave the streets of New York and other U.S. cities, to accommodate the new motor cars.

Natural gas discoveries in 1979, in the **Gulf of Paria** and 40 kilometers north of the Gulf, have once more drawn Venezuelan and foreign attention **and** investments to Venezuela's east coast. The Cristobal Colon LNG Complex, in the State of Sucre, is expected to cost $3 billion, and start up in 1997. Once more foreign oil companies (Shell and Exxon) will enter Venezuela, not as concessionaires this time, but through investments and by sharing their technology with Lagoven.

In 1920, the first Law of Hydrocarbons and Fuel Minerals was passed under President Gomez. At the end of World War I, Juan Vicente Gomez was concerned about the British, and the influence they might try to exert in Venezuela. Britannia ruled the seas during this period, as well as British Guiana on Venezuela's southern border. Gomez welcomed U.S. companies as a counterbalance to the British. Gomez's encouragement of foreign capital gave a great stimulus to exploration activity. Many U.S. companies that were still active in Mexico started to acquire oil exploratory concessions in Venezuela.

The 1920 Law of Hydrocarbons was the decisive law that encouraged foreign oil companies to enter Venezuela. It granted to the landowner, for **one year**, the right to obtain a permit for the exploration of oil and the subsequent right to obtain an exploitation concession for his property. President Gomez's goal was to have landowners sell their concessions to foreign companies. It worked! In 1921, over 2,300 landowners in Venezuela obtained concessions covering more than 18 1/2 million acres. Large oil companies then bought the concessions from these landowners, and dozens of smaller companies followed suit. An even larger number of companies were formed by stock promoters, but these soon faded. Some 73 oil companies were established in Venezuela by the end of 1924; and in December 1928, there were 108 companies registered in Venezuela, according to the Ministry of

Development. However, by 1932, only 11 companies had reached exploitation stage. Only three oil companies were really successful in Venezuela: Shell, Standard Oil (Creole), and Gulf (Mene Grande).

Since Venezuela is a big country that was relatively unexplored, there was an absence of maps. It was the foreign oil companies that not only explored Venezuela, but also mapped it, and built most of its early roads.   Geologists discovered that Venezuela has five great sedimentary basins, which cover nearly half of the country: the Maracaibo Basin, until now the most important in production; the Falcon Basin; the Apure/Barinas Basin in the southwest; the Cariaco/Margarita Basin; and the Maturin/Orinoco Basin, often called the Eastern Venezuela Basin.

The largest of the basins is the Maturin Basin where the newest discoveries of oil and natural gas fields are greatly increasing Venezuela's proven reserves and production! With deeper drilling, Lagoven and Corpoven have found fields that previously were overlooked by the old 5,000 feet limits for most wells drilled prior to 1975, by the foreign oil concessionaires. South of the Orinoco River is the ancient land mass called the Guayana Shield, which was first identified by Gene Brossard, a Gulf Oil geologist, in 1928. This is the area where Venezuela's iron ore deposits, gold and diamonds are found, but no petroleum.

The largest U.S. oil company in Venezuela was **Lago Petroleum Corporation** (Standard Oil of Indiana), which had a concession for the entire bottom of Lake Maracaibo, with the exception of the "One Kilometer Strip." The Kilometer Strip encircled the Lake one kilometer out into the water, and was where the first offshore well was drilled in 1923, and came in, in 1924. Although Lago was the **largest U.S.** oil company in Venezuela, the largest oil company in Venezuela was Shell. For years, Shell remained the largest producer in Western Venezuela.

Shell

H enri Deterding, of Royal Dutch/Shell, said that Venezuela was where he pulled off his "most colossal deal" by buying General Asphalt Co.'s (Caribbean Petroleum) huge concession, in 1912, followed by the Aranguren concession (Venezuelan Oil Concessions) in 1915.[2] The Shell Oil Companies had a big lead over other competitors. Venezuelan Oil Concessions (Shell) controlled 2 1/2 million acres in the Maracaibo Basin, encompassing the entire District of Bolivar. Producer followed producer. In 1953, Shell of Venezuela was incorporated in Toronto, as a wholly-owned subsidiary of Bataafsche Petroleum Maatschappij.

In the early days, **Shell** (VOC) was on the land (the Bolivar Coastal Field), **Venezuela Gulf** was on the Strip, and **Lago** was in the Lake. The three companies waged a drilling war, and produced 98% of the country's petroleum. By the end of 1932, there were more than 1,000 oil producing wells in Venezuela. It was Shell that contracted Schlumberger to use their new electrical coring, now called "logging," device for the first time in the Western Hemisphere, in the La Rosa field near Cabimas, and in March 1929, proved that electrical logging was an irreplaceable instrument for correlation. This tool probably contributed more than any other to the understanding of the geological details of the huge producing area of the Maracaibo Basin.

Important new technology was developed in Venezuela, e.g., off-shore drilling (British Equatorial); huff and puff steam-injection (Shell); and the first 16-inch diameter, 100-mile pipeline, in Eastern Venezuela, in 1939 (Gulf Oil). This was the largest diameter pipeline, prior to the construction, during World War II, of "Big Inch" pipeline in the United States.

The oil companies also built refineries to process Venezuela's oil: first, off the coast, on the Dutch Islands of Curacao (Shell) and Aruba (Lago); and then, in the late 1940s, they built large refineries in Venezuela (Creole, Shell, and Gulf). This enabled Venezuela to export products, in addition to crude oil, and contributed to the longevity of the foreign oil companies in Venezuela — 60 years! By the 1970s, however, there was a need to change Venezuela's refining pattern and modernize and upgrade its refineries, in order to refine Venezuela's abundant heavy crudes, and thereby manufacture lighter products.

Exploration activity by the major foreign oil companies soon raised Venezuela's **proved reserves**. By the end of 1943, Venezuela had produced 2.6 billion barrels of oil, and had 5.9 billion barrels in proved reserves. Shell had the concessions for most of the giant Bolivar Coastal field, and for years Shell remained the largest producer in Western

---

[2] Sir Henri Deterding, *An International Oilman*, (London: Harper and Brothers, 1934), pp. 89-90. Deterding was a Dutchman, who became a naturalized citizen of Great Britain in 1915, and after World War I was knighted by the British king.

Venezuela. The Bolivar Coastal field, along Lake Maracaibo, was to become the largest producing field in the Western Hemisphere, with 160 billion barrels in-place and 32 billion barrels proven reserves. In the 1980s, the reserves of the Venezuelan Orinoco Belt, with 1.2 trillion barrels in-place, and 270 billion barrels in reserves, would dwarf all the other fields in the world.

Although for many years, there were 13 oil companies producing oil in Venezuela, three had 94% of Venezuela's oil production. Creole produced 45%, Shell 32% and Mene Grande 17%. These companies share the credit for building decent housing, sanitation, medical, education and recreation facilities for their oil workers. The companies had to solve sanitation and the health problems of their workers — provide pure drinking water, and screen houses against mosquitos and malaria. Besides building hospitals, the companies had medical departments and supplied doctors and nurses. And the companies built roads! By 1950, 35% of the all-weather roads in Venezuela had been built by the oil companies.

The building and maintenance of oil camp communities has always been an operational requirement for oil producers in underdeveloped areas. In Venezuela, it was made a legal requirement. The largest and oldest group of camps is opposite the city of Maracaibo, on the eastern shore of Lake Maracaibo. The higher standard of living afforded oil workers, and the programs to prepare Venezuelan employees for increased responsibilities, added to a growing middle class in Venezuela, and contributed toward establishing a democracy.

The following were the principal Venezuelan oil workers' benefits: subsidized housing, free education for dependent children, free medical care including hospitalization, commissaries with below cost staples, free transportation when necessary, clubs and recreation facilities including golf courses, and savings plans with company contributions.

Gulf's Mene Grande

I n 1922, under the name South American Gulf Oil Corporation, Gulf Oil acquired its first concession in Venezuela. The Venezuelan Gulf Oil Company (VGO) was incorporated on March 23, 1923, as a Delaware corporation. Gulf Oil transferred all the properties of

Venezuelan Gulf Oil Co. to the Mene Grande Oil Company, C.A. (Mene Grande, or Meneg), a company it purchased in December 1936. Mene Grande was an oil company established earlier in Venezuela by a Caracas lawyer, Carlos Maury, and his associates and operated by them. The new (Gulf) Mene Grande was registered in Venezuela. (In 1952, Mene Grande was incorporated in Delaware.)

And in 1937, via a private sale, Mene Grande sold an **undivided** one-half interest in its physical properties and an **undivided** one-half interest in such oil as would be produced from its concessions in the future. The buyer of these interests was International Petroleum Company (IPC), a Canadian affiliate of Jersey. IPC did not acquire any shares of Mene Grande stock nor any control over the management of Mene Grande. The buyer paid cash for the mentioned interests and undertook the obligation to pay to Mene Grande one-half of its future costs.

Andrew Mellon (1855-1937) hired the first four geologists, who arrived in Maracaibo in 1923, among them the author's father. The first on the scene was E. E. (Slim) Boylan, as geologist and local representative. Gulf's fortune in Venezuela was assured when it acquired Creole Syndicate's concessions in the One Kilometer Strip, in 1924 (more on this in the "Jersey's Creole" section). After starting the mapping from Altagracia east to La Victoria and south to Lagunillas, Gulf started a camp at Cabimas in 1924, and the wells started to come in. The company's first producing well was completed in August 1924, a 1,800 b/d well, in the **La Rosa field.**

In 1926, Venezuelan Gulf opened up the huge **Lagunillas field** in western Venezuela, with its discovery well Lago-1. This is the largest producing oil field in Venezuela, with a total production of 11 billion barrels at the end of 1990. Later in 1926, Lago Petroleum found oil on its concession in the same region. Gulf's first oil for export was loaded in Cabimas, in January 1925. Because of the high winds in the Lake, and the land along the eastern shore subsiding with increased oil production, Mene Grande, Lago and Shell jointly built a large dike to protect their camps from the waters of Lake Maracaibo. Gulf stopped drilling activities for several years in the Lagunillas area, during which time repair work and preparation of wells for production were carried out.

Venezuelan Gulf opened up geological work on their concessions in eastern Venezuela, in 1924. Not only were oil fields with lighter crudes discovered, a Mene Grande geologist participated in the greatest oil discovery in Venezuela, the Orinoco Heavy Oil Belt, which he called "Venezuela's Black Ace-in-the-Hole."

There is a little known story of how Gulf obtained its concessions in eastern Venezuela. Addison M. McKay, a representative of the Sun Oil Company, bought concessions from an agent, who purchased them from Venezuelan landowners. McKay then sold some of these concessions to VGO for $200,000, but kept a 2 1/2 percent overriding royalty on them. McKay's helper in these negotiations was a young Venezuelan named Enrique Otero Vizcarango, whom he paid the 1/2 percent of the 2 1/2 percent he received from VGO. That 1/2 percent turned out to be a fortune and Mr. Otero used it to start one of Venezuela's leading newspapers, *El Nacional*. McKay divided up his remaining 2 percent royalty and resold it. Once VGO discovered oil in the 1930s, it realized it had made a mistake by granting the 2 1/2 percent royalty to McKay, and Gulf bought out these small royalty owners (of the 2 percent). In the early 1940s, the small royalty owners, in turn, realized their mistake, and sued Mene Grande for the return of their royalty, claiming they had been deceived. They won — and Gulf lost and had to pay them their royalties (after they repaid Gulf for their buyout).

By 1937, Gulf's activities in eastern Venezuela had become significant and this was the period of shifting emphasis from Western Venezuela to Eastern Venezuela. On May 30, 1937, the first well in the large **Oficina field**, Oficina No. 1, was completed. Between 1937 and 1940, Mene Grande built two large terminals in eastern Venezuela, at San Tome and at Puerto La Cruz. These two camps are among the most beautiful, anywhere.

Puerto La Cruz has the magnificent vistas of the Caribbean waters. It has an excellent deep harbour, and tankers were loaded at Puerto La Cruz (Guanta), either directly from the 16-inch diameter pipeline from the Oficina field, or from the Puerto La Cruz tank farm, which discharges at an elevation of 300 feet higher than the tankers. Mene Grande also built a 20,000 b/d refinery at Puerto La Cruz in the late 1940s, which was later enlarged. In 1939, Mene Grande and Creole built the 157-kilometer El Tigre (San Tome)/Puerto La Cruz highway, which runs parallel to Mene Grande's 16-inch pipeline from Oficina to the coast. This was one of the major roads that not only connected the various camps, but also serve as public highways between many cities and towns. By 1948, Mene Grande had spent $15 million building roads in Venezuela.

San Tome has a remarkable history of those who worked there, starting with the man who founded it, Gene Brossard; the great contractor who built it, Gustavo A. San Roman; and the great Swiss botanist, engineer and teacher, Henri Pittier, who supplied some of the trees. Among the many who worked in San Tome and later achieved prominence are: Jaime Lusinchi, a medical doctor in the San Tome hospital, who went on to be President of Venezuela (1984-1989); his cousin, Juan Chacin, who became President of Corpoven, Meneven and finally President of Petroleos de Venezuela; and there were others who went on to be Cabinet members; and an American, Edward B. Walker, III, who was the last President of Gulf Oil Corporation; and the most famous Gulf geologist, Dr. Hollis D. Hedberg.

As Mene Grande employees were rapidly developing oil fields in eastern Venezuela, unbeknown to them, the owners of Gulf in Pittsburgh were selling off the family jewels. Perhaps the most curious deal by the foreign oil companies in Venezuela was signed in Toronto, in December 1937. Anibal Martinez in his book, *Venezuelan Oil, Development and Chronology*, published in 1989, in England, describes an unusual agreement between Mene Grande and International Petroleum (IPC), a Canadian subsidiary of Standard Oil of New Jersey. Known to the contracting parties as the "principal agreement," it gave IPC half of the physical properties of Mene Grande and half of all future production from Mene Grande concessions in Venezuela.

In the third volume of the history of Standard Oil of New Jersey, *New Horizons, 1927-1950* (p.58), the authors explain that "International was chosen to make this purchase, rather than Creole or Lago, mainly because it had the required funds [$100 million], but also because, as a Canadian company, it seemed less vulnerable to the anti-big business attitude then prevailing in Washington."

Recent research by the author into the Mene Grande sale to International Petroleum Company reveals some rather curious reasons that motivated the transaction. According to a company lawyer, who had knowledge about the sale, in addition to obtaining capital for developing Gulf's interests in Mene Grande, the sale also created a cash fund available to Gulf Oil, which was distributed to Gulf shareholders. The Mellons largely owned Gulf Oil and the supply of cash was to help take care of estate tax following the death of Andrew Mellon in 1937, **and** to maintain the National Gallery of Art, in Washington D.C., which Andrew had built to house his superb art collection of 132 old Masters (21 were from the Czar's Hermitage collection) that he donated to the nation in the last years of his life. It was a $60 million gift, that then was the largest single donation of an individual to any government in history! (While Mellon's generosity took his children by surprise, they also later contributed generously to his and the **nation's** museum.) The National Gallery, which celebrated its 50th anniversary in 1991, has always specialized in painting and sculpture of the Western tradition — and only the very best work of the greatest artists, donated by great collectors.

Mene Grande carried the proceeds of the sale on its books as a deferred credit, which was amortized over a period of many years. The funds resulting from the sale were deposited in City Bank, San Juan, Puerto Rico, and invested by that bank in bonds guaranteed by the U.S. Federal Housing Authority and held until such time as they were needed to pay for Mene Grande's operations in Venezuela or to pay dividends.

Unbeknown to Mene Grande at the time of its sale to International, Standard Jersey opened negotiations with Shell to transfer to Bataafsche Petroleum Maatschappij (BPM) a one-half interest in the interests and obligations that International was then acquiring from Mene Grande, and which transfer occurred shortly after concluding the Mene Grande sale to International. Neither Mene Grande nor Gulf Oil were a party to the transfer by International to Bataafsche Petroleum Maatschappij, nor did Mene Grande consent to the transfer. Mene Grande considered that this transfer created no relationship between itself and Bataafsche Petroleum Maatschappij. And since Mene Grande's contract was solely with International, Mene Grande regarded the interest of BPM as merely the latter's claim against International and that no claim against Mene Grande had been created. Therefore, the Mene Grande annual budget discussions were held solely between it and International, and Shell did not attend — until 1957, when Mene Grande relented.

As a result of the Mene Grande sale, a pooling agreement in eastern Venezuela was made between Mene Grande and Standard Jersey. For economic reasons, Standard would develop Mene Grande's concessions in the state of Monagas where Standard already had established a strong operating presence, and Mene Grande would do the same for Standard's concessions in Anzoategui where Meneg was the principal producer. There was no transfer of concessions. Mene Grande traded an undivided one-half interest in its Monagas concessions for an undivided one-half interest in certain of Standard's concessions in Anzoategui.

But even less known then Gulf/MGO's reasons for selling half of their Venezuelan properties and production to Standard/IPC, is why Standard **bought** half of MGO?   Henry Linam, soon after he became President of Standard Oil of Venezuela in 1932, purchased a million acres in Eastern Venezuela for $250,000, where three major oil fields were later discovered, including **Jusepin.** And, Moses Knebel discovered the **Santa Ana** structure (an anticline) from an airplane, as did Bob Brookings spot the **San Joaquin** structure.   These two fields are in the state of Anzoategui, just north of Mene Grande's big Oficina field. SOV's activity was in the adjoining state of Monagas, where the Quiriquire and Jusepin fields were located, as was its headquarters and Camp Caripito. What better way to increase SOV's Venezuelan production then to get into Anzoategui through MGO, while they continued to expand in Monagas.

With a secret deal like the sale of half of Mene Grande to Standard and Shell, on top of the one-fifth overriding royalty Mene Grande already was paying Creole for its concessions in the Maracaibo Kilometer Strip, it is obvious that Gulf Oil's Mene Grande would never rise above 3rd place in Venezuela — behind Standard and Shell!

And how ironic it is that Andrew Mellon, who created Gulf at Spindletop in Texas, thereby shattering the Standard Oil monopoly, should have his heirs sell half of Gulf's largest producing affiliate — **to Standard Oil**, the same company that in 1902 had turned down his offer to sell Spindletop — in order to protect his art collection in Washington! By not being able to sell Spindletop, the Mellons were forced to stay in the oil business and salvage their investment in Spindletop, but as William Mellon often remarked, "That Texas oil is such a headache." Obviously, bankers are not oilmen! They have other talents. Andrew Mellon was the banker who, as Secretary of the U.S. Treasury (1921-1932), reduced the national debt by a third, and cut the Federal Budget almost in half.

Mellon left another legacy for Gulf. As U.S. Ambassador to Britain in 1932, he pressed the Foreign Office to open the door for Gulf Oil in Kuwait. In December 1933, a joint venture agreement with Anglo-Persian (BP) was reached in Kuwait with Sheikh Ahmad, and a year later the 75-year concession was granted to Kuwait Oil Company (Gulf and BP). This concession slightly made up for the loss of the concession for Bahrain **and** Saudi

Arabia (El Hasa) that Gulf transferred in December 1928, to Standard Oil of California, because of the Red Line Agreement of 1914 and 1928.

By the end of 1990, Venezuela had produced 44 billion cumulative barrels of oil. A major part of this oil came from Gulf discoveries. Lagunillas has produced 11 billion barrels, Bachaquero (1930) over 6.5 billion, Oficina 361 million, and Santa Rosa 292 million barrels. The largest producer for a Jersey discovery was Quiriquire, in the east, with 761 million total barrels, at the end of 1990. While Gulf's biggest field discoveries were in the Lake Maracaibo area, its biggest producing area turned out to be in the East on the Mesa Guanipa, where in December 1948, it produced 166,000 b/d, becoming the largest producer in Eastern Venezuela. At that time, Meneg's Eastern payroll numbered 6,503, while its Western payroll had 4,253 men.

Initially, U. S. oil companies in Venezuela followed the traditional pattern of having their headquarters in the area where they were producing. The Caracas office for many years was very small, consisting of representation in the country's capital. For Mene Grande, as for most companies, the beginning of the move toward the capital occurred during World War II, and the relocation of office personnel was **from** Maracaibo to Caracas. Chester Crebbs, as President, moved from Maracaibo to Caracas, in April 1939. The Executive department was followed by the Geological, Customs, and Land departments. With the move of headquarters to Caracas, bureaucracies were established and new office buildings were built. The workforce swelled - however, care was always needed to keep the 75% Venezuelan quota to 25% foreign employees. This was also the period when Mene Grande and the other oil companies began giving scholarships to Venezuelans to study in the U.S. and in Venezuela.

Jersey's Creole

Exxon's Creole Petroleum Corporation, which produced about half of Venezuela's oil production, was formed in 1943, with the joining of Standard Oil of Venezuela (established in 1921, as a subsidiary of Standard Oil of New Jersey), and the Venezuelan properties of the Lago Petroleum Corporation (established in Venezuela in 1923, and discussed in the next section under Standard Oil-Indiana). This gave Creole important producing areas in both the eastern and western parts of the country.

The Creole Syndicate, a group of promoters, was incorporated in March 16, 1920. It acquired lands and options in several Latin American countries, including Venezuela. The Syndicate did no drilling. It merely engaged in the buying and selling of concessions. In 1921, it acquired a number of concessions in the Maracaibo Kilometer Strip, which it turned over in 1924 to Venezuelan Gulf, in return for a one-fifth overriding royalty. Gulf's drilling in the Strip was enormously successful, which gave the Syndicate one in five barrels produced.

In 1927, Standard Oil of New Jersey concluded that the Creole Syndicate was one way to buy some production in Venezuela. Jersey had already spent more than $27 million and drilled 42 dry holes without developing any commercial production in Venezuela, and they needed new production to replace their shrinking Mexican production. And Creole was looking for funds to purchase tankers, as well as to acquire new concessions. In 1928, Jersey acquired control of Creole Syndicate, and in the complicated deal Standard Oil of Venezuela (SOV) became a Creole subsidiary, with Creole as the holding company and SOV the operating company. Creole's name was also changed to Creole Petroleum Corporation.

At the end of 1928, Jersey had only one producing well at Quiriquire, and nearly 11 million acres in concessions subject to increasing annual rentals. SOV had no geophysical department, so it hired crews from Jersey affiliate Humble, in Texas. Quiriquire was SOV's first producing field, which extended over more than 40,000 acres. The headquarters of Standard of Venezuela were moved to Caripito, the camp built to develop and produce Quiriquire. Three more fields were discovered by SOV in the 1930s, two in the west and one in the east at Pedernales, near Trinidad. SOV reduced its concession acreage to 5,250,000 acres by 1932, on the basis of findings by its exploration crews.

After Jersey purchased Lago Petroleum from Standard of Indiana, the operating management became rather bizarre. Because each of the Venezuelan Jersey affiliates had minority ownership, Jersey did not merge the two in one corporation, but from New York made its own Jersey officers top officers of its Venezuelan affiliates. Thus, Eugene Holman became President of Lago in 1932; and in 1933, he also became President of Creole. And in March 1937, the Creole directors in New York designated

Henry E. Linam as the senior officer in Venezuela and moved headquarters to Caracas. In the beginning, SOV developed in the east with Gulf's Mene Grande, and Lago developed in the West with Shell and Gulf. The official merger of Creole and SOV did not come until 1943, when it became Creole Petroleum Corporation. It was to revert back to its old name Lago (Lagoven) when it was nationalized, in 1976.

The overall importance of Jersey's Venezuelan affiliates to **Standard Oil Company (New Jersey)** cannot be overstated. By 1940, total Jersey production in the United States was 206,000 b/d, while its Venezuelan affiliates accounted for 237,800 b/d. In 1945, Jersey's Venezuelan **net** production had risen to 403,000 b/d and its reserves to over 5 billion barrels.[3] It must be remembered that this was the period of the World War and Venezuelan oil was vitally important to Great Britain and to the defense of the United States. Venezuela's oil contributed greatly to the winning of the war by the Allies. Because of this awareness by Jersey and the U.S. State Department, when the government of General Isaias Medina Angarita began to press for better statutory control of oil and gas production and to make pipelines common carriers, and most important to substantially increase the nation's income from oil production, both Jersey and the U.S. Government cooperated.

After a series of meetings arranged by the State Department, and a month-long trip to Venezuela by Jersey's Vice-President Wallace Pratt, and advice supplied to the Venezuelan government by Herbert Hoover, Jr. and his engineering firm, a new **petroleum law** became effective in **1943**. The new law raised the government's income to approximately half of the companies' net earnings from oil production; and the oil companies had their old concessions renewed for 40 years. Known as the **50-50 principle**, the company/government split in Venezuela became a model for oil development throughout the world.

As a result of Jersey's decision to enter direct negotiations with Venezuelan officials, the leadership of its Venezuelan affiliates changed. Henry Linam, President of SOV, and T.R. Armstrong, Vice-President of Creole, resigned and were replaced, by Arthur T. Proudfit, in both positions. It marked a new type of Jersey leadership in Venezuela; and in 1944, Proudfit was elected President of Creole Petroleum. He now was in

---

[3] Larson, Knowlton, Popple, *New Horizons 1927-1950*, (New York: Harper & Row, 1971), pp. 474 and 486

charge of all of Jersey's expanding operations in Venezuela.

In the 1950s, Creole's production rose to over 1 million b/d and the company employed approximately 16,000 men and women, and 93% were Venezuelan. Under the Venezuelan Labor Law of 1936, Article 17, Vol. 1, p. 236, at least 75% of a foreign company's employees must be Venezuelan. Efforts were made by the major oil companies to educate abroad, and train hard working, capable Venezuelans. At the time of nationalization in 1975, Creole had 98% Venezuelan employees out of 8,000 total.

The entire oil industry work force was 24,000 employees at the time of nationalization, which represented less than 1% of the Venezuelan work force. However, oil operations accounted for 77% of government income, and 96% of the total value of Venezuela's exports. Even in 1990, the Venezuelan petroleum industry was more heavily taxed then most oil companies in other countries. PDVSA is taxed at a rate of 85% of its gross income, actually it is around 92 percent!

Creole's stock was traded on several stock markets of the world, including the Caracas exchange. In June 1975, Exxon (name changed from SOCNJ, in 1972) took over full ownership of Creole, in which it formerly held 95% interest. They bought all of Creole's stock in order to avoid the minority stockholders from suing as a result of its negotiations with the Venezuelan Government relative to the nationalization process.

> Until that time, Exxon had chosen not to have 100% ownership so that Creole would be subject to disclosure under the stock exchange regulations. Exxon felt this would ensure that Creole's dealings would be more transparent, keep an arms-length relationship with the parent company and thereby minimize potential tax problems with the Venezuelan authorities. (as told to the author by Renato Urdaneta, former president of Lagoven.)

Exxon also did this because it felt it would have greater flexibility in developing its role in Venezuela after nationalization. Exxon wanted an ongoing role for Creole in providing technical support, services, and other assistance to the nationalized oil industry.

In the early days, as SOV (Exxon) poured their money down dry holes, Exxon's stockholders watched Lago, Shell and Gulf reap millions in Venezuela. Finally, on June 1, **1928**, SOV had their gusher — Moneb 1 — and the seven bitter, expensive years of a string of dry holes ended with the discovery of the giant *Quiriquire field*, in eastern Venezuela. Just prior to the discovery, Standard Oil of Venezuela actually purchased its first production in Venezuela, by acquiring control of the **Creole Syndicate**, on April 18, **1928** — a very important year for "Mama Creole."

But **1932** was an even better year for SOV, because SOV acquired **Lago Petroleum** and its huge concessions and production in Lake Maracaibo, along with the big **refinery on Aruba**, which Lago completed in 1929. Aruba was Jersey's first foreign plant with operations of a sufficient size to make the use of expensive new equipment economically feasible. From the time it was acquired, to the end of the 1930s, the Aruba refinery had larger crude runs than Humble's Baytown refinery, Jersey's largest refinery in the United States.

Standard Oil Company (Indiana)

here is a much overlooked historical event, which had it not occurred, Exxon might not have become a giant so quickly, and the world oil market might have been more competitive. If Standard Oil Company (Indiana) had not sold the foreign holdings of Pan American Petroleum and Transport Company to Standard Oil of New Jersey (Exxon) in May 1932, for $140 million: $47.9 million in cash and 1,778,973 shares of Jersey stock,[4] (thus, Indiana wound up owning a chunk of Jersey), it might have been Standard (Indiana) that would have been the largest producer in Venezuela — and perhaps even larger than Exxon. However, new discoveries, economics and politics in the United States effectively ruled this out.

Standard (Indiana) had acquired Pan American in 1925, from Edward L. Doheny, and it was one of the largest crude oil producers in the world. Pan American had concessions covering 1.5 million acres in Mexico, **and** 2.9 million acres *in* and around Lake Maracaibo, through its subsidiary,

[4] Emmett Dedmon, *Challenge and Response*, a Modern History of the Standard Oil Company (Indiana), (Chicago: The Mobium Press, 1984), p. 42

Lago Petroleum. Lago Petroleum started operations in Venezuela, in June 1923. And a year later, Lago was the first U.S. oil company to export Venezuelan oil. Standard (Indiana)'s "acquisition of control of Pan American Petroleum and Transport was considered the most significant event in the oil industry since the dissolution of the Standard (New Jersey) holding company organization in 1911."[5] Indiana owned 96% of the shares of Pan American Petroleum & Transport Company, which had a fleet of ocean tankers and held stock in many companies operating in several countries: Lago Petroleum Corporation, producing in Venezuela; Lago Oil & Transport Company Ltd., with extensive storage and a refinery on Aruba; Lago Shipping Co., Ltd., which carried oil from Lake Maracaibo to Aruba by tanker; Mexican Petroleum Co. and Huasteca Petroleum Co., both producing and the latter also refining and marketing in Mexico; Tide Water Export Corp. and the Caloric Co., both marketing in South America; and Ebano Asphalt Werke, A.G., in Germany.[6]

Since 1929, Pan American had been spending heavily on building a foreign marketing organization. However, under the conditions of the Depression and intense competition for markets, it was doubtful that more investments would provide adequate foreign outlets. And Pan American needed foreign outlets because the United States was practically its sole market. With the oversupply of oil in 1931, after the prolific East Texas field was discovered the previous year, a U.S. import fee appeared likely. Not only would such a restrictive measure be a calamity for Indiana's Pan American, it would jeopardize the sale of a large part of Venezuela's production, and the sale of products from the Aruba refinery. Furthermore, Indiana was aware of the possibility of their oil properties in Mexico being nationalized.

It was evident to the Board of Standard of Indiana that they needed to find a buyer for Pan American, i.e., a buyer that had an adequate foreign market and was large enough to buy this big company. Thus, they "approached **Jersey, Royal Dutch-Shell,** and **The Texas Company**."[7] Only Jersey was interested!

In 1931, Pan American's production in Venezuela was 88,000 b/d, and in Mexico 16,000 barrels a day. With the purchase of Indiana's/Pan

---

[5] Ibid., p. 26
[6] *New Horizons 1927-1950*, p. 47
[7] Ibid., 48

American's/Lago Petroleum Corp., Jersey no longer had to depend on others for its supply of foreign oil. Jersey could compete with the low-cost of other companies and supply its foreign markets. It could effectively compete in foreign countries with Royal Dutch/Shell and Anglo-Persian (British Petroleum). And Jersey could compete and grow with Venezuelan oil!

Here again the U.S. Government and the independents played a decisive role in world oil. Domestic producers, who had been successful in drilling, particularly in Texas where they brought in the huge East Texas field in 1930, pressured Congress to enact a tariff on imported crude oil and oil products, in order to force up their prices. Because of the Depression there was little demand for gasoline, and there was too much oil production in the late 1920s, and the East Texas field compounded the oil surplus.

Since Standard (Indiana) had no foreign market for its Venezuelan crude oil, or its refined products from its new 110,000 b/d refinery on Aruba, a U.S. tariff would virtually shut down its subsidiary, Pan American, which owned Lago Petroleum.

The Revenue Act of 1932 — the tariff law that Congress passed in June, (a month after Jersey purchased Pan American) — removed oil from the free list! (It was a fitting companion to the Smoot-Hawley tariff of June 1930, which ushered in the Great Depression.) The tariff, which imposed a duty of $1.05/bbl on gasoline, $1.68/bbl on lubricating oil, and $.21/bbl on crude oil, *fuel oil*, and other derivatives, set the pattern for refineries in Venezuela, until 1975. But more important, the U.S. tariffs of 1932 **restructured the oil industry**, by greatly enlarging the giant that the Supreme Court had whittled down in 1911, when it broke up Standard Oil.

The U. S. Mandatory Oil Import Program

A rthur Proudfit, President of Creole Petroleum, in his testimony before the U.S. Trade Commission in Washington, in October 1951, pointed out that Venezuela in 1949 and 1950 was the third largest importer of U.S. products, after Canada and Mexico, and Venezuela paid cash ($458 million a year). Proudfit was one of many US-American executives working in Venezuela, who over the years went to

Washington, to testify before the U.S. Congress and federal commissions, to try to prevent the independents from succeeding in their efforts to keep out U.S. overseas production. These efforts intensified on both sides in the 1950s, as oil production increased in the U.S. *and* abroad. The independents finally won in March 1959, when President Eisenhower issued the Mandatory Oil Import Program (MOIP).

The new quotas were aimed at Venezuela, whose production had just reached 3 million b/d. U.S. production was up to 7 million b/d in 1959, and imports were 1.7 million b/d. In spite of the quotas, imports continued to gradually increase over the years. Imports rose because foreign oil was much cheaper, and importers were allowed to increase imports as U.S. production rose, which it did until 1970! The MOIP quotas also led to increased imports of residual fuel oil, which is competitive with coal and natural gas, and which domestic refineries cut back, as they increased gasoline production. The increased residual oil imports came from Venezuela.

There were five, long-lasting, negative effects of the MOIP: 1) The U.S. Federal Government was now in the business of policing domestic oil prices and oil products, thereby controlling production and competition, while contributing to the lowering of the price of foreign oil. 2) Five oil producing countries, which not only lacked control over the production and sale of their oil, but also lacked control over the price of oil, decided to ban together and formed the Organization of Petroleum Exporting Countries, in 1960. 3) It encouraged depletion of domestic reserves, particularly of sweet crude. 4) It also added billions of dollars to direct fuel costs. 5) It distorted the U.S. refinery pattern, with an over emphasis on gasoline production and refinery runs of sweet, low-sulfur crude.

Venezuelan Oil Refineries

World War II made it clear to the Venezuelan government that major refineries should be built in Venezuela. The country could no longer rely on the two refineries in Aruba and Curacao for refining Venezuelan crude, nor was Venezuela benefiting from the refining on the Dutch islands. Therefore, the Medina Government, in the Hydrocarbon Law of 1943, obliged the companies to refine up to 15% of their production in Venezuela. The companies agreed to construct new refineries or to expand existing small ones. Both Creole (Amuay, 1950) and Shell (Cardon, 1949) selected the Paraguana Peninsula to build their big new refineries. Mene Grande (Gulf) selected Puerto La Cruz (1950) in eastern Venezuela, where its main production was located. Mobil built its refinery in El Palito (1960), nearer to Caracas and the industrial sector of the country. Prior to 1949, the largest refinery in Venezuela was the Caripito SOV refinery, in eastern Venezuela, which was started up in 1931.

The four major oil companies built their big refineries on the coast, in order to export their refined products. The refineries were initially built to yield bottom of the barrel products (residual products) through atmospheric distillation plants, and have small yields of white products (gasoline, etc), which might be consumed domestically. Venezuela's main market is the United States, and since the tariff of 1932 continued in effect, the oil companies designed their Venezuelan refineries to satisfy demand for residual oil in the U.S. These Venezuelan refineries complemented their U.S. refineries, which were built to produce gasoline and middle distillates, but little residual oil.

Creole commenced operating its large new refinery at Amuay, on the Paraguana Peninsula, in 1950. The refinery was built for residual fuel exports to the U.S.; therefore, its products were 62% resid, 21% distillates, 13% gasoline, and 4% asphalt. Since its large exports of residual fuel oil to the U.S. were seasonal (during the cold winter months), Creole built large storage facilities totaling **46 million barrels**. Amuay's storage capacity includes the three largest open pits in the world, totaling 27 million barrels. Open pit No. 1 at Amuay holds 11 million barrels of resid and was completed in 1955. It was the first large storage open pit in the world. Open pit No. 2 holds 9 million barrels and was built in 1956. Open pit No. 3 was built in the 1970s and holds 7.5 million barrels. The refinery was built on a cliff, composed of clay, and the pits have natural occurring walls on the ocean side. The clay is impervious to oil, and the cost of maintenance is low, compared to metal tanks.

Amuay, like other foreign oil company refineries in Venezuela, was designed to process medium crudes, and not heavy crudes, which comprise more than half of Venezuela's reserves. Since nationalization, and an investment of $1.5 billion in upgrading and deep conversion of the

630,000 b/d capacity refinery, Amuay has become one of the world's most complex refineries. Nationalization meant that the Venezuelan refineries would no longer be complimentary to the majors' refining and marketing operations.

The refineries that the foreign oil companies built in Venezuela did not adequately serve Venezuela's needs, nor did they benefit Venezuela as they should have. *First* of all, they were built to produce bottom of the barrel products, the least valuable, and often priced below the price of crude. The more crude oil Venezuela refined and sold abroad, the lower her crude sales, and therefore, the lower the revenues for the country. When President Nixon, in 1969, appointed the cabinet-level task force to review the oil import program, the Venezuelan Minister of Mines and Hydrocarbons testified and pointed out that the bulk of the U.S. purchases were residual fuel oil - priced at *16% below* crude oil. And this was when the average world price for crude oil was $1.80/bbl, and the U.S. price was $2.80/barrel.

Second, the Venezuelan refineries were built to process light and medium crudes, i.e., the more valuable crudes, which are preferable for export. However, Venezuela's reserves consisted of 20% light, 36% medium, and 44% heavy; and heavy crude discoveries continued to be larger than light crude. There was also the matter of the Orinoco Heavy Oil Belt, the largest oil reserves in the world, with API gravity crudes below 18 degrees. Venezuela's refineries had no deep conversion capacity to refine heavy oil, and the foreign oil companies had no plans to invest in upgrading their old refineries.

Third, the growing domestic market could not be satisfied, even though Venezuela had a refining capacity of 1.47 million b/d and domestic consumption of less than 200,000 b/d. There was growing demand for white products, particularly gasoline; and naphtha utilization plans, for production of petrochemical derivatives, made it essential that Venezuela upgrade its refining pattern.

A *final* reason the foreign owned refineries did not benefit Venezuela was the decline in demand for residual fuel. As more nuclear power plants were built and conservation measures reduced demand for heating fuel, the U.S. imported less residual oil. U.S. imports of residual oil peaked in 1973, at 1.8 million b/d, and started to decline, to 512,000 b/d in 1985. U.S. demand for resid dropped from 2.8 million b/d in 1973, to 1.19 million b/d in 1985.[8]   Thus, Venezuela's resid exports to the U.S. dropped from 595,000 b/d in 1973, to 151,000 b/d in 1983.[9]   In a U.S. refinery, the average yield of residual fuel oil from a standard 42 gallon barrel of crude is 7% per barrel.   In Venezuela, the yield for residual was 64% per barrel in 1974, declining to 33%/barrel in 1983, after upgrading.

The **petrochemical industry** (Petroquimica de Venezuela) was started by the Government of Marcos Perez Jimenez in 1956, with the construction of the Moron Complex, near Puerto Cabello.   **Pequiven** (under PDVSA since 1978) has three complexes, the second is El Tablazo on Lake Maracaibo, which was started in 1969.   The third is now being developed in eastern Venezuela, the Oriente Complex, at Jose near Puerto La Cruz.   Pequiven has two subsidiary companies: Petroplas that manufactures and markets polyvinyl-chloride resins (PVC), and Fosfaven that is responsible for mining rock phosphate, in the state of Falcon.   Pequiven also participates in over 16 joint capital ventures with Venezuelan and foreign investors.

The petrochemical affiliate of PDVSA had a $3.2 billion expansion program underway, to be completed by 1993, of which $1.5 billion was to come from private capital.   Unlike the oil industry in Venezuela, the petrochemical industry was started by the Venezuelan Government and was never under the control of foreign companies.

Oil Profits

U. S. oil companies in Venezuela made large profits every year on their operations. Creole Petroleum's profits in 1951 passed the $200 million a year mark and continued upward, reaching $300 million in 1955. Creole became the brightest jewel in Jersey's crown, accounting for more than 40% of Standard of New Jersey's total net income.

After 1948, the large oil profits were divided 50-50 with the Venezuelan Government.   The *50-50 formula* shaped the dynamics of Venezuela's economic growth.   The new increase in government revenue resulted in an increase in the purchasing power of the population.   In

---

[8]   *Monthly Energy Review*, DOE/EIA, December 1985, p. 53

[9]   *Data on Petroleum and Economy of Venezuela*, Lagoven, Caracas, issues of 1979 (Table 17), and 1983 (Table 18)

December 1958, the Provisional Government headed by Edgar Sanabria raised oil taxes from 50 to 60 percent so that the government would be able to balance the national budget in 1959, and in future years.

The foreign oil companies made billions of dollars on their exports of Venezuelan oil. But the Venezuelans, prior to 1948, received very modest returns. On an accumulated production of *1.1 billion barrels*, between 1917-1935, Venezuela's total fiscal income was *$92 million!*[10] Compare this 19-year period, with Venezuela's oil revenues in 1974 of $9.4 billion (after OPEC raised the price of oil), and 1980 of $11.6 billion, and one is given cause to wonder at the paltry return this country received for the first 30 years of production when foreign oil companies produced its nonrenewable resource.

Because of the many years that the Venezuelan people did not realize an equitable share of the profits from the extraction of their natural resource, some understandable anger was built up in men like Romulo Betancourt, President of Venezuela (1959-1963). Betancourt recounts in his book, *Venezuela, Politica y Petroleo*, about a trip he made to the National Gallery of Art (Mellon-Gulf Oil) in Washington, and how he visualized a little plaque under each masterpiece with the following inscription: "A present from the Venezuelan people to the capital of the United States." Had he known how these paintings cost half of Mene Grande's production after 1937, he might have added another inscription.

Venezuela's dependency on one industry controlled by foreign capital, i.e., foreign oil companies, reached such a point after 1935, that it became difficult for the government to freely make decisions regarding the oil industry without affecting the national economy. Venezuela had commenced a policy of "sowing the petroleum." And after 1970, the cuts in oil production (because of a world oil glut), and the decline in reserves, curtailed the government's spending plans and contributed to a budgetary deficit in fiscal year 1972.

The famous Venezuelan scholar, Arturo Uslar Pietri, coined "to sow the petroleum means to utilize the wealth which Venezuela receives from the oil industry in developing other sources of production." President Lopez Contreras (December 1935 - May 1941) set out on a program of improvement, and to finance it he looked to the government's oil rev-

---

[10] Luis Vallenilla, *Oil: The Making of a New Economic Order*, Venezuelan Oil and OPEC, (New York: McGraw-Hill Book Co., 1975), p. 39

enues. His program was continued by successive administrations. The results of *sembrar el petroleo*: thousands of miles of highways, vast housing projects, hundreds of schools, hospitals and clinics, the conquest of malaria and other diseases, irrigation, dam and electrification projects, **and** agricultural programs.

The diversification of Venezuela's economy placed the country in an enviable position in the late 1950s. Venezuela had **no national debt** and it paid cash for what it purchased. In 1957, Venezuela's purchases of goods and services from the United States alone exceeded $1 billion. More than 1,500 U.S. companies sold products and services to Venezuelans.

Nationalization

After 1974, Venezuela had the needed capital to respond to the foreign oil companies' power to counter any new regulation or tax proposal, by threatening not to invest, *or* cut production. The nationalization law of the oil industry in Venezuela, Decree No. 1123, was signed by President Carlos Andres Perez, on August 30, 1975. Not the enterprises, but their assets, would become the property of the State, on January 1, 1976. Employees of Petroleos de Venezuela (PDVSA) and their integrated petroleum affiliates would not be civil servants. The law reserved to the State all activities relative to the exploration, exploitation, refining, and marketing of hydrocarbons. The compensation arrived at for the 22 concessionaires was $1.01 billion.

The U.S. Department of State decided that the transfer of private U.S. properties to the Venezuelan Government was satisfactory, because there was fair compensation (net book value) and due legal process. And Venezuela's President Perez assured the U.S. that Venezuela would continue to sell oil to the U.S.

The State Department wanted the United States to rely on Venezuela for oil, rather than on the Middle East or Africa, because it was a dependable supplier and politically stable. There has never been an interruption in the flow of Venezuelan oil, either in times of war or in times of peace. The Defense Department deemed Venezuelan oil as secure as seagoing domestic oil, because the Caribbean and coastal waters are "now significantly more secure than the high seas." Although attempts had been made in the past to keep out Venezuelan oil, when Venezuela nationalized the oil industry, there was some concern in the United States. Until the early 1970s, Venezuela was the largest source of U.S. oil imports (and became so again in 1986), of both crude oil and products.

Unacknowledged and forgotten, by the Nixon and Ford Administrations, was Venezuela's increased oil exports during the Arab oil embargo. Instead of gratitude, the U.S. Congress responded by including Venezuela in the exclusion of OPEC members from the "generalized system of preferences" attached to the Trade Act of 1974, adding injury to insult. Developing countries were to be helped by expanded trade and imports, **but Venezuela** was to be punished for her help during a "crisis."

The principal foreign crude oil producers in Venezuela in 1975 were: Creole, Shell, Mene Grande, Sun, Mobil, Continental, Atlantic Richfield, Standard of California, and Texaco. Occidental was accused by a former Oxy official of having paid over $3 million in bribes and political contributions to electoral candidates and government officials, and was denied compensation in 1975. (In October 1989, the Venezuelan Government agreed to pay Occidental $42 million in return for Oxy's dropping its 15-year old lawsuit against Venezuela and the U.S. Trade Representative's petition that Venezuela be excluded from the General System of Preferences.)

In 1975, Venezuela exported 759,000 b/d to the United States, out of 2.3 million b/d production. In 1973, Venezuela had exported 1.2 million b/d to the U.S. Concern for Venezuela's exports *after* nationalization were expressed by former Ambassador Robert McClintock, in an annual country assessment paper in 1975, in Washington. The recently retired Ambassador to Venezuela recommended that the State Department take a more active role in direct negotiations with Venezuela concerning oil - prices, levels of production, and the share channelled to the U.S. market - rather than leave the negotiations to the private U.S. companies. But this wasn't the Middle East, and the companies did not want any help. Furthermore, the companies were anxious to sign: 1) purchase agreements for oil from their former owned companies, and 2) technical assistance agreements, which they believed would pay handsomely!

Nationalization does not take place simply because political parties on the left strongly push for the take over of a foreign company or industry. There are reasons that occur, which make the action advisable to a government, even though there may be strong opposition to the nationalization within the country, as there was in Venezuela. When nationalization takes place in a country, the government makes compensation to the owners of the property that is taken over. When expropriation occurs, which is the act of dispossessing the owner of a property, no return on investment is made.

Mexico's expropriation of the oil companies in 1938, is often used as an example of expropriation of the industry. However, Mexico was not the first to expropriate oil companies - the Bolsheviks in the Soviet Union were the first, in 1920. Furthermore, Mexico did eventually settle with all of the oil companies (Royal/Dutch Shell, Standard of New Jersey, the Sinclair group of companies, and Standard of California) once they agreed to deal with the Mexican government. The last payment on the *$165 million* total indemnity was made in 1962. (Gulf Oil was the only oil company whose affiliate was not expropriated in 1938. Maximo Diaz, a Cuban American, later negotiated the sale of the Gulf property in Mexico.)

Since exploitation on private lands, under Mexico's system of accession (prior to the 1917 Constitution), did not generate any sharing by the nation in oil profits, Mexico did not fundamentally depend on oil. Oil revenues amounted to 10% of Mexico's national revenue. Expropriation, therefore, did not disrupt the national economy or bankrupt the National Treasury. Furthermore, Mexico's oil production, which started in 1901, peaked in 1921 with 550,000 b/d, and steadily decreased, until in 1938 it was only 105,000 b/d. The loss of foreign markets after 1938 did not unduly disrupt Mexican production, because Mexico's domestic oil consumption amounted to 46% of total production. The country had become industrialized and somewhat diversified.

The oil companies in Mexico learned that when a judgement is rendered by a foreign arbitration board, and is sustained by the country's Supreme Court, that workers' social benefit demands should be met, you do not become intractable over a difference of $1 million. The government of Gen. Lazaro Cardenas did not set out to expropriate the oil industry. Mexico lacked technical personnel, tankers to transport her oil and an international marketing system - all of which the foreign oil companies had. After nationalization, Mexico also faced interference from the United States and British governments through diplomatic channels. And World War II soon broke out, and German submarines sank most of Mexico's small oil fleet.

The Fourth (or Third) Largest Petroleum Company

W eighing a variety of factors, including volume of reserves, production, refining capacity, operations integration and sales, as well as investments, earnings and personnel, *Petroleum Intelligence Weekly* classified Petroleos de Venezuela, S.A. the fourth largest oil company in the Western World, after Saudi Aramco, Royal Dutch/Shell Group, and Exxon, in 1988 and 1989. PIW ranked PDVSA third in 1991, after the Shell Group! The Venezuelan oil industry made great strides in the 1980s.

After nationalization, the first order of business was to gain markets abroad, and build up Venezuela's production and reserves, which had declined after passage of the Reversion Law of Concessions, in 1971. Under this law, all the assets, plant, and equipment belonging to the concessionaires within or outside the concession areas would revert to the nation without compensation upon expiration of the concessions, in 1983. The law also required the concessionaires to deposit funds in Venezuelan banks to guarantee (known as the Guarantee Fund) that the assets would be kept in good working order.

Decree 1123, signed by President Perez, on August 30, 1975, provided for the creation of a public corporation called **Petroleos de Venezuela, S.A. (PDVSA).** PDVSA's main objectives were to be planning, coordination and supervision of all owned affiliates. The relationship between the holding company and the operating companies was meant to be the same as that which had prevailed between the former concessionaires and their foreign holding companies. Creole Petroleum, now called Lagoven, would report to PDVSA, just as Creole had reported to Exxon in New York. PDVSA was the owner of all of the shares of the 14 operating companies that were nationalized. And the state was the shareholder of the PDVSA shares, whose representative was the Minister of Energy and Mines, who set oil policy for the industry and appointed the PDVSA Board.

In organizing the structure of the new Venezuelan oil industry, the three major producers, i.e., **Lagoven** (Creole), **Maraven** (Shell), and **Meneven** (Mene Grande/Gulf Oil), became three of the four operating companies, with the fourth operating company created in 1978, and

RESTRUCTURING OF THE VENEZUELAN OIL INDUSTRY

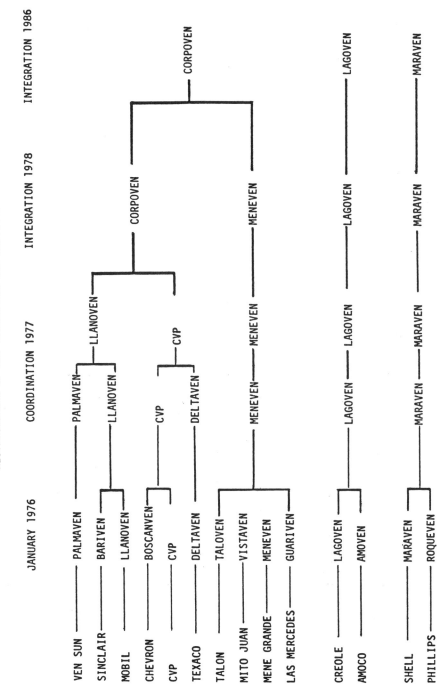

named **Corpoven**. The smaller companies were absorbed into the larger ones. Corpoven was created out of CVP (Corporacion Venezolana del Petroleo), the state oil company and an appendix of the Ministry of Mines and Hydrocarbons, which was formed in 1960, during the Romulo Betancourt administration. In addition to CVP, five more small companies were added to Corpoven. The consolidation of the original 14 operating companies in Venezuela was achieved without a break in operations. (See the following chart on: Restructuring of the Venezuelan Oil Industry.)

There was a further consolidation in 1986, when the operations and installations of Meneven were integrated into Corpoven. It was rather ironic that Gulf Oil Corporation was taken over by Chevron in 1984, in the U.S., and the old Gulf company in Venezuela disappeared two years later. At the same time that Meneven ceased to exist, there was also a reassignment of operations among the three remaining companies, in order to have larger operation areas, as well as three operating companies of a similar size: **Lagoven, Maraven** and **Corpoven.**

During the 1980s, the industry grew in many different directions, domestically and overseas! At the time of nationalization, only Maraven had any experience with international markets, because Shell has always had a policy of allowing more local control than U.S. companies do with their overseas subsidiaries. Thus, only Shell Venezuela had international experience in selling their production and had an international trading department. The other companies sold their Venezuelan production through the trading channels of the multinationals. After nationalization, the Venezuelan oilmen did the logical thing: Maraven oil traders moved into the other companies and trained the men and women in the new international marketing departments about the world oil trading market. As expertise was acquired, it became evident that PDVSA should invest in foreign downstream refineries and distribution systems that were complimentary to their oil production.

Interven, originally created to administer PDVSA's joint downstream venture with Veba Oel in Germany, was also changed in the 1986 restructuring to oversee the new joint ventures in the United States. The purchase of **Citgo Petroleum** was under negotiation at the time, and the purchase for 50% ownership, closed September 30, 1986. In January 1990, PDVSA bought the remaining 50% from Southland Corporation. PDVSA also purchased 50% of **Champlin Refining and Chemical Inc.**, in March 1987, and later in January 1989, bought the other 50% from

Union Pacific Corporation. In April 1991, Interven was split up, forming **PDV America Corp.**, and **PDV Europa**.

In September 1990, PDVSA announced it would fold Texas based Champlin into Citgo Petroleum Corporation, headquartered in Tulsa, Oklahoma. In the United States, PDVSA also has a 50% joint venture with Unocal Corp.: a refinery in Illinois and a supply agreement. The joint venture is called **Uno-Ven**, and was formed, in October 1989. A fourth U.S. refinery purchase was made in 1990: a 50% interest in **Seaview Petroleum**, a 84,000 b/d asphalt refinery in New Jersey. In March 1991, PDVSA purchased the other half of Seaview.

The merger of Champlin (150,000 b/d refinery) with **Citgo** (320,000 b/d refinery) makes Citgo the eighth or ninth largest refiner in refined product sales volume in the United States. In 1989, Citgo had 517,000 b/d of refined products sales, and Champlin had 201,00 b/d, since some of the Venezuelan oil product exports are marketed through their U.S. refineries. After acquiring these two big refineries in the United States, PDVSA had, up to 1990, invested $445 million in safety and upgrading projects; and over the next five years planned some $2 billion in investments in further upgrading and to meet new U.S. environmental standards. The combined 1989 sales revenue of the two U.S. refineries was close to $7 billion, proving that the foreign investments were prudent. Furthermore, Citgo was ranked by *Fortune*'s "500" issue in 1990, as the third most productive in sales per employee for 1989. And three months later in July, Petroleos de Venezuela was ranked the **second** most profitable on returns on assets, in *Fortune*'s "Global 500."

PDVSA's first overseas downstream joint ventures were in Western Europe, with Veba Oel, and the formation of **Ruhr Oel**, in 1983. The joint venture processes Venezuelan heavy crude for the German market. It combined Venezuelan capital and heavy crude with the German marketing strength of Veba. Veba Oel A G is West Germany's (now Germany) state controlled oil company. Ruhr Oel has two refineries and 20% interest in two other German refineries, for a total capacity of 500,000 b/d, and two petrochemical complexes and distribution systems.

The second PDVSA European joint venture was signed in 1986, with Sweden's Axel Johnson, purchasing 50% of **A B Nynas Petroleum**, a company processing and distributing asphalts and lubricants. Nynas owns two small refineries in Sweden, one in Belgium, with total processing capacity of 55,000 b/d, and an extensive distribution system in Western

Europe. In 1989, Finland's Neste Oy purchased the 50% owned by the Swedish partners in Nynas and thus became partners of PDVSA.

In 1985, Royal Dutch/Shell decided to shut down their 320,000 b/d refinery in Curacao, after failing to obtain an acceptable pricing formula from Venezuela for heavy crude, following heavy losses during the previous four years. At the time, there were five big export refineries in the Caribbean, all running at half, or less, of their capacity. These refineries were built to process fuel oil, or residual, for U.S. utilities and factories that, by 1985, had switched to cheaper and cleaner natural gas. The refineries on these Caribbean islands were the biggest moneymakers, and , closing them down would bring enormous hardship to the island economies and to all of the people out of work. Exxon was the first to close down its 420,000 b/d refinery on Aruba, in March 1985. They were followed, in June, by Charter Co. and Chevron's Borco refinery in Freeport, Bahamas (now PDVSA's).

Shell's Curacao refinery was going to be closed on September 30, 1985, unless a solution was found. The refinery provided 30% of Curacao's gross national product and there were fears of political turmoil (Cuban) in an island close to Venezuela's principal refineries and their Lake Maracaibo oil production. A rescue formula was worked out by the government of Venezuelan President Jaime Lusinchi and the Minister-President of the Netherlands Antilles, and signed on September 26, 1985. Shell agreed to transfer ownership of its Curacao refinery to the island's government, and Venezuela agreed to operate the refinery under a 5-year lease for a fee of $11 million per year. **Refineria Isla, S.A.**, a new affiliate of PDVSA began operating the 320,000 b/d refinery, on October 1, 1985.

Venezuela's refinery capacity has doubled through its overseas acquisitions. Domestic refining capacity is 1.2 million barrels a day, with 4 large refineries and one small refinery. Overseas, PDVSA has 11 refineries, plus the Curacao refinery, with total capacity of 1.5 million b/d. With this large refining capacity, PDVSA has become a traditional oil company, selling oil products rather than crude oil.

In 1989, PDVSA acquired **Bonaire Petroleum Corp.**(Bopec), a transshipment/storage company in Bonaire, Netherlands Antilles, 50 miles off Venezuela's northwest coast. PDVSA thus acquired 9.5 million barrels of storage, as well as a deepwater port with a displacement of up to 500,000 dwt to receive supertankers. Venezuela has no deepwater port.

This storage capacity, plus the Bahamas,' acquired in 1990, and the Curacao refinery's storage, gave PDVSA 34 million barrels total offshore storage in the Caribbean. With this storage capacity, PDVSA acquired better operational and strategic flexibility in the international market, as well as assuring customers of the proximity of supply. PDVSA now controls three of the six major oil terminals in the Caribbean. (Aruba has 11 million barrels of crude storage, and Trinidad has 8 million.)

Chevron sold its mothballed (since 1985) 500,000 b/d Borco **Bahamas** refinery to Lagoven/PDVSA, for $120 million. Lagoven was interested in the 20 million barrels of storage capacity. However, in the future the refinery may be revamped, since it is offshore Florida, and it is nearly impossible to build a new refinery in the United States.

Among the **many** accomplishments of the Venezuelan petroleum industry during the 1980s, two stand out. The **Eastern Venezuela Cryogenic Complex** was built by Meneven and started up, in November 1985. The complex utilizes the new discoveries of natural gas to produce some 57,000 b/d of liquids, which are mostly for export. At the time it was finished, it was the largest cryogenic complex in the world. The second major accomplishment was the discovery by Lagoven, of the giant **El Furrial/Musipan** field, in 1985. This discovery, with proven reserves of 2 billion barrels, permitted the re-interpretation of the regional geology of the Maturin Basin with the possibility of finding additional deep fields that may contain 20 - 30 billion barrels. The F-M field is the largest discovery of light crudes in 30 years. Venezuela has 230 active oil fields, with production expected to be up to 1970 levels again in 1995, i.e., around 3.5 million b/d.

Due to capable managers and executives in the operating companies, and the efficiency of their operations, the Venezuelan Government turned to PDVSA to take over and run other state industries. The first was the petrochemical industry, which had always operated in the red. In a few years, the oilmen turned the petrochemical industry around, modernized it, made it profitable, and started it on a rapid period of growth.

PDVSA's affiliates continue to increase in number. The first one was **Intevep**, created at the founding of PDVSA — and the subject of this book! Others soon followed: **Petroleos de Venezuela (USA) Corp.** and **Petroleos de Venezuela (Europe) S.A.** to provide intelligence from these two centers for Venezuelan oil, petrochemical, bitumen and coal trading. **Pequiven** (1978) is responsible for the petrochemical industry. **Bariven** (1980) coordinates overseas purchases for the industry. **Refineria Isla** (1985) was created for the Curacao refinery (and in 1991 was given the Borco terminal). **Carbozulia** (1986) was created to develop the Guasare coal mines in the state of Zulia. **Interven** (1986) was formed to oversee the downstream foreign joint ventures, but was divided in 1991, to form two new companies: **PDV America Corp.** as the owner of Citgo Petroleum Corp., and the 50% of Uno-Ven; and **PDV Europa, B.V.** acquired the European downstream joint ventures.

Palmaven (1988) was created to distribute fertilizers to the local market and give technical assistance to the Venezuelan agricultural sector. **Bitor**-Bitumenes Orinoco S.A. (1988) was created to develop and market the bitumen resources from the Orinoco Belt. **Cepet** (1983) is the management and training center for the industry. **PDV Marina**, created in 1990, is responsible for the operating companies' tankers and marine activities. The Venezuelan petroleum industry now has around 47,500 employees, excluding employees of foreign downstream companies.

The 1990s

At the end of 1990, Venezuela had produced a total of 44 billion barrels. The history of the Venezuelan oil industry in the 1990s will surely be very different then what it was in past decades. It will be a **global** industry and it will rely more and more on its natural gas reserves for domestic consumption and for exports. Venezuela's exports will comprise of: oil products, crude oil for its overseas refineries, Orimulsion from the Orinoco Belt, coal, petrochemical products, and LNG.

Liquid natural gas (LNG) will be produced from the reserves in the Caribbean, north of the Gulf of Paria, and will be exported. The **Cristobal Colon LNG Complex**, in the state of Sucre, is expected to cost $3 billion, produce 700 MMcf/d, and start up in 1997, with two trains.

The new joint venture company will consist of: Lagoven, S.A., with a 33% share as owner of the gas and operator; Royal Dutch/Shell Group, with 30% share will provide drilling and processing technology; Exxon, with 29% will handle marketing of the gas in the United States; and Mitsubishi, with 8% will contribute transportation expertise. The LNG project has been assigned to Lagoven by PDVSA. Lagoven discovered the dry gas reserves in the Gulf of Paria, in 1979.

After drilling 14 wells, the proved reserves were 4 trillion cf, however, these reserves are expected to rise to 20 trillion cf after the 55 planned wells for the project are drilled. The four to eight offshore platforms, wells, and pipeline will cost over $1 billion; and the liquefaction plant and terminal at Mapire, on the Peninsula of Paria, on the Gulf of Paria, will cost around $1.3 billion. Three new LNG tankers, costing about $200 million apiece, will be used to ship the LNG to the U.S. East Coast or Gulf Coast, the nearest market for Venezuela's LNG.

The four gas fields are about 24 to 27 miles offshore in the Caribbean Sea. PDVSA needs outside technology and capital to develop the huge offshore gas fields discovered in deep water (around 400 feet). But first the Venezuelan Congress had to act on PDVSA's request to form this joint venture.

The Natural Gas Nationalization Law of **1971** *prohibits* foreign joint ventures or private investments in natural gas operations, as well as LNG plants for export of products. Under the 1971 law, Corporacion Venezolana del Petroleo (CVP) established in 1960, could produce associated gas only, but no nonassociated gas. However, "under Article 5 of the Oil Nationalization Law of **1975**, the LNG project can be accommodated," according to Renato Urdaneta, former President of Lagoven, and since his retirement in October 1990, the first chairman of the Cristobal Colon LNG project. The Venezuelan income tax law was changed in 1991, so that this project, as well as other future associations, would pay income tax under the 30% tariff, the same applicable to other industrial commercial activities. Unfortunately, the Colon Project was not detached from the hydrocarbon tax bill, and therefore, the effective tax rate would be much more than 30% after you add in royalty payments (15% of the value of gas extracted) and Fiscal Export Values. (Tax reference values were first applied to the foreign oil companies under the 1966 Income Tax Law, whereby the Executive set oil prices for income tax assessment purposes.)

LNG exports from Venezuela did not make economic sense in 1971, when there was surplus gas production in the United States, and surplus oil production in OPEC. Conditions have now changed, and LNG is the only proven technology that enables gas reserves to be produced and exported overseas.

Trinidad

T he close proximity of Trinidad to Venezuela has meant a close relationship in the development of their petroleum industries. Trinidad and its offshore areas occupy the eastern extension of the Eastern Venezuela Basin. The recent discovery of giant oil fields in the Maturin sub-basin of Eastern Venezuela has renewed interest in Trinidad's very complex geology. Trinidad's national oil companies, late in 1989, signed a 5-year oil exploration agreement with Exxon, Chevron and Total CFP, to explore onshore Trinidad's southern oil belt for deeper horizons thought to be analogous to nearby Venezuela's El Furrial trend.

The $70.5 million exploration program was to cover 65% of onshore Trinidad, at depths of 8,000 to 17,000 feet. Known as the Southern Basin Consortium, Exxon will be the lead company with 20% interest, and Trinidad & Tobago retain 51% interest in any oil found. New discoveries are necessary, because enhanced oil recovery techniques are not enough to maintain Trinidad's declining oil production, which peaked in 1978, at 230,000 b/d, and by 1990 had declined to 150,000 b/d. Geology of the area causes decline rates of 30-35% per year.

Commercial production started in Trinidad with the discovery of Forest Reserve, in 1914, the same year that Shell started commercial production in Venezuela. Oil production in Trinidad exceeded Venezuela's, until 1923. By 1974, Trinidad had produced 1.4 billion barrels and reserves were 2.5 billion barrels. Standard Oil of New Jersey entered Trinidad in 1928, by acquiring Trinidad Oil Fields Operating Company, Ltd. (This was the same year that Jersey acquired Creole in Venezuela.)

Long before their oil production commenced, Trinidad was exporting natural asphalt from its famous Pitch Lake, discovered by Sir Walter Raleigh. Trinidad's first company was Trinidad Leasehold, which started exporting asphalt in 1896.

Trinidad is about seven miles from Venezuela at the nearest point. And, had it not been for, first, French, then Dutch, and finally British control, which was established in 1802, Trinidad would have been a Venezuelan island, like Margarita. Columbus named the island after the three hills he sighted on reaching it, in 1498. Spanish settlers arrived in 1532, and the Spanish name for the capital still remains - Port of Spain (Puerto Espana).

Venezuelans are a peaceful lot and the Trinidadians have never felt threatened by their close proximity — geologically and geographically separated only by the small Gulf of Paria. Modern history might have been quite different, however, if both had gained their independence from Spain. Columbus' discovery of Venezuela in 1498, at sight of the Peninsula of Paria, the "Land of Grace" as he called it, and his discovery of Trinidad the same year, resulted in **one** Spanish colony. However, when Venezuela gained its independence from Spain in **1821**, Trinidad was a new British colony, and Trinidad and Tobago did not became independent until **1962**. In spite of the political separation, the influence of the petroleum industry has been dominant and often parallel in both countries.

Oil did not become the dominant industry in Trinidad until the 1940s. (It was also when the famous steel bands first appeared, using old oil drums.) Before and during World War II, Trinidad was the largest oil producing center in the British Empire, and, therefore very important in the British war effort. The Shell Group's associated company in Trinidad was United British Oilfields of Trinidad Ltd. (UBOT), and it along with other companies in Trinidad drained their oil fields beyond maximum efficient rates, in order to meet the war needs for oil.

Offshore exploration began in the 1950s, and the Soldado field was discovered in 1951. Offshore fields now provide about 80% of Trinidad's oil production.

Trinidad may eventually become a larger natural gas producer than oil producer. The Caribbean plate's southeastern boundary is in eastern Venezuela and Trinidad, known as the El Pilar fault zone. A fault that taps the source rock when it is generating oil can lead to an oil accumulation. However, a fault that taps the source rock when it is in the metagenesis stage can yield only gas condensate. Since 1972, a series of large gas fields have been found on the Atlantic coast of Trinidad, in deeper offshore areas, where no major oil fields are located. Amoco Trinidad Oil Co. discovered the major Cassia gas field, in 1982. Before this, Amoco was producing associated gas from the Teak and Poui fields off Trinidad's southeastern coast. Cassia gas field is south of Poui. Gas discoveries have also been made off the north coast of Trinidad by a consortium comprising Deminex, Agip, Tenneco, Occidental, and Trintoc, the national oil company founded in 1974, when the state took over Shell's interests.

For 15 years, Amoco was nearly the sole producer of natural gas in

Trinidad. The National Gas Transmission Co. has sole responsibility for gas transmission and distribution, **and** the National Energy Corporation has a monopoly of gas purchases and sales. Furthermore, the Ministry of Energy and Natural Resources has overall responsibility for the regulation of oil and gas. In Trinidad, natural gas is used for injection in oil wells to maintain production pressure, however, the major consumers of gas in Trinidad are the electric power industry, and the industrial sector. Trinidadians have also considered adding an LNG plant to their industrial park at Point Lisas, on the west coast.

It appears, however, that it will be the Venezuelans who build the first LNG plant off the Gulf of Paria to tap into Venezuela's huge gas reserves - close to Trinidad. And possibly the Cristobal Colon LNG company will some day buy Trinidadian gas for its liquefaction plant. In 1989, Trintoc and Pecten were successful bidders for two blocks in the Trinidadian OCS, in the Gulf of Paria, and Lagoven bought into the Trintoc block.

Venezuela and Trinidad have a long tradition of working **together** when it comes to territorial waters and oil drilling - longer and friendlier than other countries generally have. (On Venezuela's western border, this was not the case with Colombia over the Gulf of Venezuela.) In February **1942**, when German U-boats torpedoed tankers off the Venezuelan coast, Venezuela and Britain signed an international treaty delineating the submarine areas in the Gulf of Paria. It was the **first agreement** relating to the **Continental Shelf.**

Finally, some background on Venezuelan oil exports during World War II, and other wars =

U.S. oil companies were in Venezuela by 1922, starting to develop its enormous oil reserves. In 1928, Venezuela became the leading exporter and the second largest producer, after the United States. Venezuela's production was 289,000 barrels per day and the United States' production was 2 1/2 million b/d, in 1928.

During World War II, Venezuela's oil exports were around a half million b/d, and the U.S.'s and Venezuela's oil exports were the vital supply in tipping the scales of victory in favor of the Allies. **It was in the inter-**

est of U.S. national security to have access to Venezuelan oil. Tankers were being torpedoed by German submarines (U-boats) off the Venezuelan coast to stop Venezuelan oil from reaching the United States and its allies. Some 50 U.S. tankers had been removed from their regular voyages and were put into a shuttle service carrying crude and oil products from Venezuela, Aruba and Curacao, and the U.S. Gulf Coast, to New York and Halifax where the oil was transshipped to British tankers.

After September 1939, when World War II began in Europe, the Venezuelan flow of oil to Europe was shut off **temporarily** by the German blockade set up at that time. In 1941, the United States started importing more oil from Venezuela to send to the Allies. However, the Caribbean was no longer safe for oil tankers from Venezuela moving north, nor for Venezuelan oil being refined on Curacao and Aruba. In addition to torpedoing ocean tankers, the Nazi submarines shelled the two refineries off Venezuela's coast that were built to refine Venezuelan oil (produced by Shell and Standard Oil).

Winston Churchill wrote in his book, *The Second World War - The Hinge of Fate*: "In the Caribbean Sea, amid a wealth of targets, the U-boats chose to prey chiefly on the tankers." "The interruption of this traffic would affect our whole war economy and all fighting plans." (pp. 110, 109) **Venezuela's oil helped float the Allies to victory in World War II.**

Furthermore, after the Japanese attack at Pearl Harbor, Venezuela helped the United States by opening its ports and air fields to U.S. and allied naval vessels and aircraft. Venezuela supplied the United States with oil during the Korean War and the Vietnam War. And during the Arab oil embargo, following the 1973 Arab/Israeli war, Venezuela increased its oil exports to the United States. In doing this, during the Arab oil embargo, and particularly during World War II, Venezuela overproduced some of its oil fields (i.e., it produced at a rate **above** maximum efficient rate, or MER) in order to supply oil to the United States!

Venezuela now has the largest reserves of oil, and the second largest reserves of natural gas, and the largest reserves of bitumen, in the Western Hemisphere! This country can no longer be ignored, nor taken for granted.

CHAPTER IV

INTEVEP'S MASTER PLANS AND GROWTH

When a hundred generations have mixed the powder of their bones with the dust of the forest, it will be seen that in the memories of glory there has been no one greater than Bolivar. (inscription on Bolivar's statue, in La Grita, Tachira, Venezuela)

T he small group of men who launched Intevep may be remembered for important accomplishments in their lives, but none of these will be greater than the founding of Intevep. The first four years of Intevep was a race to find a site to build their research center, then to start building, order the necessary equipment, and most important, recruit Venezuelan researchers in a country that had not fostered research. In the latter objective, they were fortunate to be able to get 78 first class

researchers from IVIC, i.e., from the Petroleum and Petrochemical Group that had been organized, in 1973. But even here, a dispute arose over IVIC letting them move to Intevep.

When the Petroleum and Chemical Center was formed in 1973, within the Technology Research Center (Centro de Investigaciones Tecnologicas), at IVIC, the funding came from the Ministry of Mines and Hydrocarbons through FONINVES (which was established in 1974, to fund research and training in hydrocarbons). The Petroleum and Chemical Center, formerly named the Petroleum and Petrochemical Department, moved to Intevep, in **July 1977**. The head of this group, Dr. Nestor

Barroeta, and Jose Luis Calderon, moved to Intevep on December 1, 1976, to begin preparations for the Center's move. The decision for the move was made by the Perez Government, in order to centralize the programs in oil refining and production research in Venezuela. Carrying out this decision, however, was not simple.

The Director of IVIC, Dr. Luis Carbonell, appointed in 1974, by President Perez, was not anxious to have the Petroleum Center move to Intevep, because its departure would leave a vacuum and weaken IVIC's research capabilities. Dr. Carbonell, in an interview with the author in November 1989, said that the creation of the petroleum institute was necessary, and that it should be outside of IVIC. However, "they should have paid for the laboratory equipment that they took." Thus, it was not only that the researchers were leaving IVIC, it was all of the laboratory equipment that followed them that made their departure doubly objectionable to Dr. Carbonell and IVIC. This disagreement between Dr. Barroeta and Calderon Berti on Intevep's side, and Dr. Carbonell and his group, spilled into the Venezuelan newspapers, between July and December 1976.

While the departure left a vacuum in IVIC, the move of the Petroleum and Chemical Center to Intevep was essential, in light of the scarcity of oil researchers in Venezuela. Dr. Barroeta's group formed the core of researchers in the formation and growth of Intevep. Had it not been for this well trained and capable group of scientists, Intevep would not have acquired the running start it achieved in its research on the Orinoco Oil Belt, which became its most important project. Some of this research on extra heavy oil was started at IVIC. But here too, Intevep would face problems, because the Ministry of Mines and Hydrocarbons controlled the Oil Belt, and PDVSA could not appreciate the need for heavy oil research. To the rescue, Calderon Berti did another end run on General Alfonzo and his Board and not only got the Oil Belt research project for Intevep, but also the transfer of control of the Belt from the Ministry, to PDVSA. The Ministry's techical staff wanted to retain operational control of the Belt, however it was the industry that had all the resources to conduct operations.

Besides hiring scientific personnel, Intevep needed to educate itself on setting up a first class research institute. Therefore, key people were sent abroad to train and study at major oil company research centers, research institutes, and universities. Already waiting in the wings to help was Dr. Stewart Blake, who had been Evanan Romero's professor at Stanford, and was to have an important hand in organizing Intevep in its formative years. At this time, Dr. Blake was Vice President of Stanford Research Institute (SRI). Dr. Blake had already submitted a preliminary Master Development Plan to Invepet, in September 1975. And after it became Intevep and came under PDVSA, a fully developed Master Plan of Development was submitted, in July 1977. (Another comprehensive updated Master Plan was presented in October 1982, and the fourth, in 1991.)

Along with the necessity of acquiring researchers, there was the selection of a site, and the building of offices/laboratories and a library, for the researchers. Unfortunately, there was a division among the supporters of Intevep over whether to locate Intevep in Los Teques, or in the West, in the state of Zulia near the City of Maracaibo. Five possible sites were identified: 1) Ciudad Fajardo (Valle Guarenas-Guatire), 2) Terrenos de la Universidad Metropolitana (La Urbina), 3) Ciudad Lozada (Valles del Tuy), 4) Urbanizacion La Fragua (near IVIC), and 5) Terrenos de Villa Pignatelli (Los Teques).

In July 1976, certain requirements for a proper site were defined in a report, by a Commission headed by Humberto Calderon Berti and appointed by the President's Council of Ministers. The Commission (consisting of Calderon Berti, representing the Ministry of Mines and Hydrocarbons; Jesus Lachman, representing the Engineers of Zulia; Vianney Villegas, Ministry of Public Works; Rafael Caceras Perera, Ministry of Sanitation and Social Assistance; Jose Martorano Battisti, PDVSA; Dr. Pedro Obregon, CONICIT; and Dr. Luis Carbonell, IVIC) was formed to study the feasibility of using the **Villa Pignatelli** in Los Teques as the site for Intevep. The Commission considered the following requirements: 1) proximity to the decision makers in the industry, 2) availability of professional and scientific personnel, 3) with enough distance from the day to day operations of the industry, so as not to distort its own activities, 4) sufficient proximity to urban centers to assure good communications, schools, housing, recreation and cultural activities.

The Villa Pignatelli filled these requirements and a few additional ones. It **had a building** that could be adequately remodeled in a year, thus **saving** precious **time** in getting Intevep started, and therefore, **money** spent on new technical assistance contracts (CATs) with the foreign oil companies. The first contracts were for two years, and would be under discussion, again, in 1978. The Venezuelan oil industry would be in a stronger position to discuss technical assistance if they had a functioning petroleum research and development institute that would later bear fruit. It should be noted that the departing foreign oil companies originally asked for 25 cents a barrel for technical assistance when discussions were held in 1975.

Another advantage that Pignatelli had for Intevep was its central location in Venezuela — on the outskirts of Los Teques, State of Miranda, and 25 kilometers from Caracas; as well as the 87 hectares, with 35 of these being usable for new buildings for future development. The Villa Pignatelli was near IVIC, i.e., a few miles further along the Pan American highway, in the same mountain range. The Villa was small by comparison to the imposing mountain that Humberto Fernandez-Moran had obtained for IVIC, in 1955. [With other adjacent purchases over the years, Intevep's land would grow to over 700 hectares.]

It was a stroke of luck that the Jesuit monastery/seminary, the Villa Pignatelli, was suddenly on the market. Due to declining numbers of young men entering the priesthood, the Jesuit seminary was used less and less and the Church decided to sell it. Actually, it was available because Diego Arria, Governor of the Federal District, had a fight with the Jesuits over their land. The Perez Government was negotiating to build a workers' housing project. An argument over the matter occurred in the President's Cabinet, and the Villa became available for Intevep. When General Alfonzo was asked about the Villa as a place for Intevep, he said PDVSA would not buy the site. However, in a written opinion submitted to the Commission appointed to choose a site for the new organization, PDVSA stated that it supported the selection of Villa Pignatelli for the reasons the Commission gave, as well as for other reasons, e.g., some of the new operating companies had not signed CATs with their former owners and needed Intevep's help. PDVSA also stressed the need to get a functioning Intevep to help in evaluating the CATs, and for this purpose a central location like the Villa was preferable.

But there was strong opposition from CONICIT, and Western Venezuela, that is from the oil producing state of Zulia. A group of influential officials in Zulia sent a letter to President Perez objecting to Villa Pignatelli and citing the reasons they thought Intevep should be in Zulia. Their arguments revolved around the fact that Zulia was the principal oil producing region in Venezuela, and therefore, the largest number of engineers and professionals were located in Zulia. The letter, dated March 18, 1976, was signed by the Archbishop of Maracaibo, the rectors of the universities, president of the Chamber of Commerce, in all, by 48 leaders of professional groups, unions, and business groups.

CONICIT was represented on the Commission by their president, Pedro Obregon, who did not sign the final report, and submitted his dissenting report, on July 19. Curiously, CONICIT objected to the reasons for getting Intevep started, rapidly, i.e., in time to have Intevep evaluate the CATs. CONICIT was under the impression that it was *their job* in certain specific cases, and the Ministry's, FONINVES's, or PDVSA's responsibility to evaluate CATs. CONICIT also objected to spending 20 million bolivars (around $4 million) **and** remodeling the Villa.

But nothing was going to stop Calderon Berti. He would get his site, the Villa Pignatelli, near the center of power in Caracas. The official letter to establish Intevep at the Villa Pignatelli was sent by the Minister of Mines and Hydrocarbons (by Hernan Anzola, vice Minister, for Valentin Hernandez, Minister) on **June 16, 1976,** to the Commission appointed to study the Villa site. In the second and last paragraph, Minister Anzola, points out how important it is that Intevep start functioning quickly, **and** that it **be sufficiently advanced** when negotiations for the new technical assistance agreements commence. Thus, Intevep's Villa Pignatelli had two important forces working in its favor: Calderon Berti, and the costly CATs.

It is fitting that the final site selected for Venezuela's petroleum research institute was a Jesuit monastery in the mountains. The Jesuits for centuries have been the great teachers in our Western civilization, and they were often in the center of advances and changes. Intevep was near the decision makers; able to attract experienced scholars and scientists; distant enough from daily operations to maintain their independent research; but near enough to urban activities for good communications and services. The site selection for Intevep has contributed to its success. It is near the oil power (the Ministry), near intellectual centers (the many universities in Caracas), and cultural activities (orchestras, and museums).

And what happened to the Jesuit priests at Villa Pignatelli? They retained a small piece of land, where they built a new, smaller monastery. It is across the Quebrada de la Virgen (Ravine of the Virgin) within sight of their old monastery, which has been turned into a black glass cube — housing the executive offices of Intevep.

Objective of Intevep

I n the July 1976 report of the Commission charged with the study of the Villa Pignatelli as the site (Sede Central) for Intevep, the following is stated as the **fundamental objective** of Intevep: to provide technology for the national petroleum and petrochemical industries, in order to reduce to a reasonable level their technological dependency on foreign resources.

This report and the other studies, Master Plans, for Intevep made clear that it was too costly to ever achieve near or total technology independence from foreign resources. Furthermore, it was not realistic, with available human resources and physical resources. Thus, Intevep's objective from the beginning was to strive to reach a level in technology comparable to other important petroleum producers. These planners clearly understood that the newly nationalized oil industry needed a strong technological support system, in order to guarantee continued efficiency.

The Venezuelan oil industry needed personnel who would be capable of evaluating the technical assistance being offered by the multinationals. As one Venezuelan oilman, who the author interviewed, put it: we needed experts who not only understood what was inside the "black box," but could help us fix it when it broke. The customary way was to sell the needed technology (black box) without repair instructions, therefore, when something went wrong, the Venezuelans had to wait until someone flew in from abroad to fix it. This was a very costly way of acquiring new technology.

Along with performing this important technical service to the operating affiliates of PDVSA, Intevep also started its own basic research programs. However, before it could start this research, on the Orinoco Oil Belt and continental offshore, which was suggested in Invepet's *Diagnostico*, Intevep needed a good library and laboratories for its researchers.

Prior to becoming Intevep, the fledgling Invepet started by defining **three** projects, from which later grew the first three divisions of Intevep. The *first* project was the Technical Library of Hydrocarbons, which became the Center of Technical Information (CIT), in the Division of Technical Services. The *second* project was the Center of Geophysical Data Processing, which became part of the Department of Earth Science, in the Division of Exploration and Production. And the *third* project was the Laboratory of Lubricants and Additives, which commenced the Department of Petroleum Products, in the Division of Refining and Petrochemicals. These three projects basically set the pattern of research for Intevep, as well as its organizational structure.

In some respects, the gaining of approval of a site for their Sede Central, or headquarters, and hiring their researchers was simpler than gaining acceptance and approval of PDVSA's affiliate oil companies. Fortunately, the CATs pushed them through the door and established their membership in the petroleum club!

CATs — Technical Assistance Contracts

As stated by Dr. Stewart Blake, in a January 1980 report for Intevep:

The original concept for Intevep was quite limited in scope and envisioned Intevep operating as an Institute with primary concentration on maintaining a center of knowledge regarding technical matters in the petroleum research and development field. This was a limited concept in that the operating companies were intended to rely heavily on technical service agreements with major foreign companies for operational technical support as well as for advanced technical services.

W hile the Venezuelan government was opposed to paying large sums for technical assistance to major foreign companies (ex-concessionaires), the operating affiliates of PDVSA knew that getting their technical assistance from their former concessionaire was essential in maintaining operations.

On the other hand, for the foreign oil companies, the first CATs were a politically disguised way of increasing asset compensation, which from a legal position could not be greater than book value. Later CATs were to be more realistic and reflect technical benefits derived from them. It should be emphasized that the CATs were *service* contracts and *not* technology sharing agreements.

In the beginning, in 1976, there were 14 nationalized operating companies, which were different in size, and technical know-how. Three of the 14 were small Venezuelan oil companies: Mito Juan, Talon, and Las Mercedes. It was understood that the smaller companies would eventually be fused with the larger ones, and PDVSA would wind up with four operating companies. The first stage was *coordination*, with a great deal of consultation among the oil companies. A committee of PDVSA Board members was formed in 1976, to study ways in which reorganization of the operating companies could be accomplished. By 1977, the process was in motion to absorb the smaller companies into the larger ones (Lagoven, Maraven and Meneven), and in **November 1978**, the fourth largest company was created by fusing CVP and Llanoven (Mobil) and creating Corpoven. (Please see chart on restructuring in Chapter III.) This was all accomplished without a break in operations.

The process was important for several reasons: it increased uniformity of administrative systems and procedures, and eliminated years of past intense rivalry and secrecy, by adjusting working conditions, and using the HAY-MSL job evaluation system (applied globally in the industry). It also made it possible to exchange technical, as well as administrative information. No longer would the Venezuelan oil industry have *nine* technical assistance contracts (CATs) as they did in 1976, e.g., Llanoven with Mobil, Deltaven with Texaco, Palmaven with Sun Oil, Boscanven with Chevron, etc., because these companies were now merged with the four large operating companies. There would no longer be a duplication of services purchased, and therefore, the cost of technical assistance would be reduced.

Thus, as Intevep was getting organized to become *the* research institute of the Venezuelan oil industry, the industry itself was getting organized and would be better able to make use of Intevep's capabilities and potential. They went through growing pains at the same time, and once through this period, the operating companies could profit from Intevep's research efforts.

From the limited original concept for Intevep, its increasing capabilities were utilized by the operating companies to replace some foreign sources of advanced technology. Its range of technological support services to the Venezuelan oil industry greatly increased, along with its provision of information to other parties in Venezuela. Over the years these services have grown.

The first technical assistance contracts (CATs), the ones that commenced in 1976, were to assure the continuing operations of the petroleum industry after nationalization. These CATs were negotiated by the Ministry of Energy with the concessionaires that were departing Venezuela. The Venezuelans were not negotiating from strength, because their oil companies had little or no technology development capability (nor international marketing experience, except for Shell/Maraven). After World War II, when the multinational oil companies built big new laboratories in the United States and in Europe, technology was exported. Each multinational shared its technology and research differently with its overseas affiliates. However, when it came to selling their technology to a *former* company it was for cash on the barrel. The shareholders of the foreign companies that were nationalized in Venezuela asked for $.25 a barrel for their assistance. This was negotiated down to $.14, after learning of the

$.10 a barrel Kuwait paid for technical assistance after it nationalized Gulf Oil and British Petroleum's Kuwait Oil Company, in March 1975.

The first CATs were negotiated with payment based on barrels of oil produced and processed by each Venezuelan affiliate. However, with the renegotiations with Mobil in late 1977, a new form of payment was worked out, based on the use of agreed upon services. And in 1979, when the Venezuelan operating companies signed technical assistance contracts with engineering firms, an additional form of payment was introduced based on the salaries of the personnel used by the firms, as well as renumeration of actual costs. Payment was not made on barrels of oil.

Venezuela paid an average of **$350 million per year** on CATs for the first contracts **between 1976-1979**, and $158 million between 1980-1982. The costs were reduced 45% between the first and second contracts, due to better contractual conditions and the gradual reduction of the basic fees of the five principal contracts with British Petroleum, Exxon, Gulf, Mobil and Shell, **and** because they diversified and contracted engineering firms like Bechtel, Williams Brothers, Heyward Robinson, etc.. Note that after 1979, diversification of companies supplying technical assistance included non-former concessionaires like British Petroleum (and in 1981, Total).

And, because there were now only four operating companies, instead of the 14 original companies, only Exxon, Shell, Gulf and Mobil signed new CATs, with Lagoven, Maraven, Meneven and Corpoven respectively. The PDVSA affiliates did their own negotiating on their new CATs, which commenced January 1, 1980. By signing earlier contracts, in 1979, with the engineering firms and BP, pressure was put on the ex-concessionaires to be more accommodating than they had been in 1975. Furthermore, total world capability for providing oil technical services to those needing it increased in the later half of the 1970s. Technical assistance was not unique to the oil companies.

The second group of CATs eliminated a number of onerous and restrictive clauses in the 1976 CATs; among them *confidentiality* was eliminated, i.e., information could now be shared with the other operating affiliates **and** Intevep. And equally important, under these CATs, the affiliates were going to receive much more technical information, and of higher quality. As the former president of Lagoven explained to the author: "Confidentiality was something very dear to the heart of companies like

Exxon because they felt that if technical information and manuals were freely exchanged among the companies, sooner than later that information would leak to the other international oil companies rendering similar services. The potential for `technical contamination' was judged to be too great."

With Intevep established when the second round of CATs were under discussion, the foreign multinationals did not have the upper hand (and get $.14 per barrel produced or refined, as they did in 1976). But there is probably a more important reason for the decline in the cost of CATs, and that is the conclusion of the Lagoven/Exxon MPRA (Modificacion del Patron de Refinacion de Amuay) project for the upgrading of the Amuay refinery, which cost $1.5 billion, for deep conversion processes. This Lagoven project accounted for a major portion of the cost of technical assistance contracts between 1976-1981. Both the Amuay and the El Palito (Corpoven) refinery upgrading projects were completed in 1982. Fluor was the prime contractor for Amuay.

The first contracts covered exploration, production, refining, natural gas liquids (NGL), transportation of crudes, and other areas related to operations. At the time, Venezuela had little exploration going on, as the foreign oil companies had practically shut down this operation in Venezuela. As for NGL, there were few companies in the world with NGL processing installations. (But Venezuela was about to build the largest cryogenic complex in San Joaquin and Jose, and inaugurate it in 1985.) Among the areas related to operations, covered in the 1976 CATs, was management consulting, which consisted of establishing management systems in the administration of oil industry operations, as well as the evaluation and structure of human resources, salary compensation, budgets, and industrial security, etc.. However, only under the Shell CAT did the management consulting cover actual training. Shell, by far, gave Maraven the best technical assistance contract in 1976.

After reading through a 158 page confidential report on CATs written by an ad-hoc oil industry group at PDVSA, in the spring of 1983, one understands that the foreign oil companies that were nationalized on January 1, 1976, quickly made up their loss with the technical assistance contracts they signed with PDVSA. While many foreign oil workers departed Venezuela, about 300 staid on in their old positions, for there were no ready replacements. The foreign oil ex-concessionaires created service companies to run their technical assistance contracts. Contracts were signed with all of the previous concessionaires (with the exception of Atlantic Richfield), mostly for four years. Until their usefulness ran out, these service companies were cash cows!

And yet, without the CATs it is estimated that the productivity of the Venezuelan industry would have decreased by 10 to 20 percent, as Gustavo Coronel points out (p.86), in his book, *The Nationalization of the Venezuelan Oil Industry*. Coronel also points out that at the time there was decreased world oil demand and lower tanker rates, which made Middle East and African crude oils very competitive. And Venezuela's old producing reservoirs made production a difficult task, for which they needed help from the ex-concessionaires.

The CATs made it possible to obtain important technical services, but **no new** technology, during the period when ownership of the oil industry in Venezuela was being transferred from the foreign petroleum companies to the Venezuelan nation. "It is difficult to see how this transition could have occurred without the technical services secured by these agreements," wrote Stewart Blake in a report on Technical Services Agreements, in February 1978. In spite of the essential help, Dr. Blake went on to list the weaknesses the CATs represented from Venezuela's point of view. The first CATs were heavily biased in favor of the supplier of technical services.

1. There was no incentive for the foreign suppliers to provide their latest discoveries, or technologies, in order to improve the efficiency of production and refining.
2. The payments formula was complex and cumbersome. The payments were tied to the volume of production, i.e., the price to be paid was based on the daily average number of barrels of crude produced in certain fields, plus the daily average number of barrels of crude processed by certain refineries and modified by consideration of taxes, etc., would determine the total payment.
3. An escalation clause used to determine the price paid for technical services was tied to variations in the Capital Imported Product Index, which is a part of the General Wholesale Price Index for Venezuela. The way this clause was written, inflation in Venezuela would provide windfall profits or increase in payment to the foreign oil company.

4. CATs only covered narrowly defined services. Needed new technology was not covered. CATs covered only the provision of routine technical services needed to maintain the status quo. Here, Dr. Blake points out the problem with the confidentiality clause. "There is no reason why the government of Venezuela should not be able to use technology which it has bought and paid for, in any of its petroleum operations in-country."

5. Some of the specifications were one-sided. For example:

a) the cost of services, trips, were determined unilaterally by the foreign oil company's service company; and

b) the information that the parent company or its divisions gave to its service company operating in Venezuela. The PDVSA operating affiliate got only what technical information the service company had.

6. The purchasing provision was no longer of value, because the affiliates had acquired this needed experience. Furthermore, it could make them subject to lawsuits in the United States because under this provision the Venezuelan company was completely responsible to vendors for all aspects of the purchasing operations conducted by the service company.

Finally, there is the difficulty of determining the true cost to the service company of providing a technical service. Competitive bidding is a far better way of procuring technical services and reasonable costs.

Can these services now be provided in Venezuela? Can Intevep provide these services? Dr. Blake concludes that the Venezuelan industry needs objective advice and assistance on matters of petroleum and energy policy.

> The advantage of Intevep is that it is a new uninvolved organization which does not have a history of long, personal and professional relationships with either the operating companies or their parent companies. It is also uninvolved insofar as other sources of technology are concerned, and thus can bring the petroleum industry advice and assistance which could be very useful in making these important decisions.

An important contribution that Intevep has made to the Venezuelan petroleum industry is the development of the capability to evaluate foreign technology that the affiliates want to purchase. In some cases, the affiliate discovers that Intevep has the needed technology, and it is not necessary to buy it abroad. They can purchase it from Intevep. But sometimes they do not, preferring foreign resources. Acceptance does not come easily.

Master Plans

When Humberto Calderon Berti, Evanan Romero and their colleagues were going to meetings at PDVSA and the affiliates selling their technical services and the need to develop new technology in Venezuela, particularly in heavy oil, they were also carrying out their Master Plans at Intevep.

There have been four Master Plans. The first two were put together for *Invepet* in 1975: the Master Development Plan; and the Master Operations Plan. These were 5-year general plans, which Evanan Romero presided over, and Dr. Stewart Blake and G. L. Garvey assembled. Dr. Stewart also introduced William L. Pereira Associates, the California architects, to the Invepet founders. By having these two Plans when Invepet became Intevep, they were able to "hit the ground running." They not only knew what they needed, they were organized, and had a team determined to succeed. In addition to the two Master Plans to guide them, Intevep had the *Diagnosis of Technology Transfer in the Petroleum Industry*, which Invepet had produced. (see Chapter II, "Intevep's Creation") The Master Plans would guide them in building the best research facilities, while the *Diagnosis* would guide them in the research that the Venezuelan petroleum industry needed.

Most of the goals in the Master Plans were accomplished during the last 15 years. The most important consideration in developing the Master Plan was accommodating growth in response to changing technological demands in Venezuela. The building program was to accommodate a future 1,200 employees at the headquarters location, where it would have 44,050 square meters of building space. [Actually, the total space grew more than 250% over the area originally planned — to over 128,350 square meters. And by 1992, the number of employees had grown to nearly 2,000 because new research programs were added.]

Ground breaking at Villa Pignatelli was between November 1976 and February 1977, with the actual **move** occurring in **July 1978**. The first executive to have an office at the monastery during the building period was Dr.

Nestor Barroeta — in a building shed. He was followed by the researchers and technicians from IVIC. The first two professionals hired were Alejandro Villoria, who got his Masters in Petroleum and Motors, at the French Institute of Petroleum, in 1974, and Jesus Bilbao, who got his Masters in Physics at Arizona State University, in 1973. Villoria became manager of Petroleum Products, and Bilbao was in charge of Geophysical Data Processing.

Alejandro Villoria started, with the help of research and engineering firms, the first new specialized laboratory building — for petroleum products. The new **Petroleum Products** building was divided into three principal areas with laboratories for: motor bays to evaluate lubricants and motor combustion of gasolines and diesels; field testing; and product additives. The Products building was finished in **July 1982**, and became the fourth and best equipped in Latin America. The other three were at Brazil's CENPES, the Mexican Petroleum Institute, and at Argentina's YPF. Intevep's modern Products building cost 24.6 million bolivars and the equipment cost another Bs. 23 million. The additional Workshops and Warehouse cost Bs. 26.1 million.

There was a great need for the department of petroleum products because products is the reason for the production of crude oil. Motor vehicles are the largest consumers of petroleum products, therefore, it was necessary to study and improve gasolines, diesels and lubricants used in these internal-combustion engines. The Intevep petroleum products researchers concentrated on fuels, lubricants, solvents and waxes, and on asphalt (Venezuela produces some of the best in the world). The Venezuelan oil industry was forced to develop this technology because with petroleum products you run into proprietary information, as Armando Izquierdo, section manager in the Department of Petroleum Products told the author during an interview. Each integrated oil company develops its own products plus the additives for particular markets. Foreign companies had their chemical companies to produce their additives, which are covered by patents. Venezuela has good weather, no winters, therefore, has no need for winter weather driving gasoline, or very high viscosity index motor oils.

Research at Intevep, therefore, would be in *content evaluation* and *improvements* of gasoline. The products department needed help from other departments, in particular the analytical chemists to break and define the gasoline components. Next, the products department needed to get *performance evaluation* of the gasoline, which involves more expense. Simulation screening tests using car engines, and field tests using employees cars, or car rentals, were used. All of this was necessary because they could not purchase this technology, since patents are not applied for in petroleum products as they are not patentable! You can purchase refinery processes but not product patents.

Because gasoline usage is so important, and for all of the above reasons, the Lubricants and Additives Laboratory project was started in 1975, in Invepet, at its Centro Empresarial, Los Ruices. This group was among the first to arrive at the Villa Pignatelli, when ground breaking was started on the Central Headquarters. Villoria's group simply moved into the construction workers' shacks. Their working quarters were quite modest before moving into their new Petroleum Products building, in 1982.

The remodeling of the monastery, i.e., the first section of the Central Headquarters, was finished before commencing the building of the Petroleum Products laboratories. The offices in the Central building included offices for administrative and management support; offices for research personnel with and without laboratory facilities; areas of common services: computer room, library, conference rooms, cafeteria, auditorium and an infirmary. The infirmary was essential considering the location of Intevep up in the mountains. In this first phase, the technical library (CIT) was built, costing Bs. 3 million.

In addition to the CIT, and the Laboratory of Lubricants and Additives, a third project, the Processing Center for Geophysical Data was started in 1976. And once Nestor Barroeta's group from IVIC arrived the following year, research activities commenced in refining processes, exploration and production, the offshore program, transportation of crudes, **and** heavy crudes.

Winston Peraza was the General Coordinator of these early plans, acting as organizer and financial planner. Evanan Romero took care of research in production and transportation, and Nestor Barroeta was in charge of refining and chemistry. And the technical managers were: Eli Schwartz, general engineering, Frank Ashford petroleum engineering, and Enrique Vasquez, earth sciences. Paulino Andreu, who had also been at IVIC, arrived in 1977 and spent 10 years at Intevep, first heading up Intevep's catalysis section, and in 1980 became general manager of the refining and petrochemical division. Stewart Blake was the principal adviser to Calderon Berti and the Board, prior to 1979. It was a struggle — but it was the best of times!

After the Villa Pignatelli site was selected, the William L. Pereira Associates were given the task of preparing a preliminary master plan for the site. The **Master Plan of Development, July 1977,** laid out three principal functional components for the *space requirements* of the headquarters complex.

First, the **Administrative Center,** which would house "management of the research activities and for those researchers who do not need direct access to laboratory space, together with such central support facilities as the Technical Library of Hydrocarbons, a computer center, meeting rooms, and food service facilities." (p. 6)

Second, the **Specialized Laboratories** were the next construction project, which were "high bay industrial space." These laboratories are required to conduct research involving heavy and bulky equipment and possibly hazardous materials. The Petroleum Products building and Mechanical Workshops were the first specialized laboratories built, and after these, the small pilot plants were built. Construction commenced on the Petroleum Products building after the Evaluation of Crudes Laboratory was finished in July 1980, which was the first of the nine prefabricated modules.

And, the *third* principal component for space requirements were the **General Laboratories**, which is "flexible space provided with all laboratory services, suitable for bench work in such areas as analytical chemistry and geology, together with research offices."

Construction moved steadily: from the remodeling of the seminary, which started in January 1977, and was finished in December 1979, with the Auditorium, but with personnel starting to move in during **July 1978;** and continuing with new additions and new buildings; to the principal access road of 1.5 kilometers; to proceeding with the prefabricated modules; to the National Guard Command; to Workshops, Warehouse, and Petroleum Products; to utilities; and to the recently finished General Laboratories. It was a carefully planned growth, for research facilities, and for development of research projects.

Growth in Land

The Administrative Center is actually in the center of a plateau, with the Specialized Laboratories to the north of it, and the newer General Laboratories on terraced land to the south, directly below the three-story black cube where the executive offices are located. After you exit the Pan American Highway and as you enter the gate at Intevep, you travel up the mountain and all of these facilities are on the left. And on the right, on two higher knolls, are located sport fields for their employees, general storage, and an area for guest housing and recreation. On the highest knoll are located Intevep's utilities, including gas, and a water tank (3,000 cubic meters capacity, a 10-day water reserve), and maintenance functions. Each of the two knolls on the right have a service road that forks off from the main road up the mountain.

The former monastery/seminary building was located in a dominant position on a plateau in the center of the site. The 20-year old building, a four story reinforced concrete structure, provided a total of 10,700 square meters of area. The site slopes down to a ravine, which crosses the site diagonally from northwest to southeast. At the bottom of the ravine, known as La Quebrada de la Virgen, is a small stream, which is lined with trees. The entire site has wonderful vistas of mountains, trees and vegetation, birds in flight, and fresh air. There is some farming in the area, and Intevep, on land purchased later, has several experimental farms, growing oranges and coffee, etc. Among the trees on the site were stands of eucalyptus trees on the hills above the monastery.

In 1978, reforestation was started on many hillsides to prevent erosion, and to return the whole area to its natural state that existed many years ago before the railroad came, and before foreign trees, like the eucalyptus, were planted. In the first phase of the program, 130,000 small trees were planted, and they are continuing with about 30,000 trees per year.

Intevep purchased the upper hills overlooking the Villa Pignatelli, which is in the river basin area of the Quebrada de la Virgen. Most of this land was covered with natural vegetation, and not eroded by urban sprawl. It is an important environmental area. Without these land purchases, Intevep soon might have been surrounded, from above, by the precarious shacks of squatters as the city of Los Teques grows outward. Besides the Villa Pignatelli, Intevep purchased 12 other parcels of land; the largest was Hacienda El Carmen. The total price for these other 12 land purchases was 46 million bolivars.

Particularly significant was the Presidential Decree, No. 515, in 1980, making the area surrounding Intevep, **Basin of the Virgin Protected Zone**, and assigning the regulating of this zone to the Minister of the Environment and Renewable Natural Resources. However, two years later the Ministry of the Environment had not issued the new regulations protecting this **green zone**.

The **landscaping** concept was established in the 1977 Master Plan of Development. Intevep had areas replanted that were cleared in the building process, planting species native to the area. And they landscaped gardens and parks with flowers, bushes and trees. Furthermore, in 1981, Intevep initiated a Master Regulator for Green Areas, i.e., an ecology air filter system, using the greenery of trees on the hills around Intevep to filter out incoming pollution.

Growth in Facilities

A minimal amount of recontouring for site development for new buildings was needed at the Villa. The General Laboratories, which came under the first phase of the Master Plan, but were not finished until 1990, are known as **Sur I and Sur II**. Of the new buildings, these two required the most recontouring — on two hectares of site development. The two large connecting-buildings were to house laboratories and offices for analytical chemistry, geology, catalysts, petrochemical, and the new environment and ecology division, etc. These new, modern laboratories are state of the art, certainly the finest in Venezuela, and among the best in the world.

The 32,000 square meters of lab and office space in South I, and South II are joined to facilitate communication and interaction. The two buildings are grouped around the service yard to provide many of the laboratories with adjoining outdoor work space; and the labs are serviced from a central utilities distribution zone, which can service laboratories on either side. All offices are located on the exterior of the building for light and a view, with labs right across the hall.

In addition to the Special and General Laboratories, Intevep has had

Field Laboratories for specific projects. These were small labs near the site of operations in the field where Intevep researchers were working on special projects, like the first one, at Amuay for gasolines, another in Barcelona for the Offshore Project, and the ones at Maturin and Jobo for Intevep's research on the Orinoco Belt. Only the Jobo laboratory is currently maintained, for intermittent projects. The others were dismantled once the research projects were concluded. The purpose of the lab at Jobo is to assist the affiliate operators on the service work and research that is necessary during evaluation programs and execution of pilot projects on Orinoco oil.

An unusual facility (unusual that is, in the United States), which Intevep built at its headquarters, is the **National Guard** center located near the road leading up to the laboratories and offices. In order to protect the petroleum industry's installations in Venezuela, the government has posted the National Guard at all major facilities. Intevep has 20 Guardsmen permanently posted, with room for 35 in case of an emergency.

Intevep also has a **Fire Station** for volunteer firemen, to protect the buildings and facilities, as well as, the surrounding hillsides where fires might be started in the dry season. They have two fire trucks with special capabilities to put out 70 degree steep hillside fires, and another modern fire truck with high pressure water strength capabilities to put out fires in buildings. They have a water supply truck, too. And, near the Fire Station, Intevep has a heli-pad for helicopters to move personnel, in case of an emergency.

Becoming a Company and an Affiliate

In 1979, the Board of Petroleos de Venezuela, including President General Rafael Alfonzo Ravard, in an Extraordinary Assembly, voted to change Intevep into a **mercantile company**. This meeting occurred on *May 25, 1979*, following two prior meetings, one at PDVSA on May 10, and the other on May 24 at Corpoven, authorizing this action. Thus, on **May 31, 1979**, Intevep was registered in the Federal District, and in the State of Miranda, as an affiliate company of Petroleos de Venezuela. Its new name was **Intevep, S.A.**, but much more than its name would change.

In retrospect, it was more of a profound change than imagined at the time. It appeared to give Intevep researchers a more equal footing with the operating companies and financial security. But for that added financial security, there was a price to be paid — a certain loss of freedom for the researchers. With the departure of Calderon Berti, and the arrival of Nelson Vasquez as the new president of Intevep and new Board members to turn Intevep into an efficient company, Intevep would become part of the rotation system for oil executives. PDVSA chose to emulate Exxon and their "arabesque," rather than Shell, which has not used its research centers as a lateral move for executives.

The researchers at Intevep not only lost some freedom by having oil operations men supervise them, they also lost research time, because they now have to deal with a company bureaucracy, layers of management, and countless committees and meetings. This obviously puts enormous stress on a scientist/researcher. His lost time in meetings has to be made up later. The oil companies, because of greater government demands, controls and regulations, and endless audits, are making more and more decisions via committees; and the industry has become more complex.

Intevep had presented **a report** (Bases Para La Clarificacion de la Mision) on its mission and objectives to PDVSA, in **October 1978**. It was an analysis of research in the petroleum industry, its relationship with the affiliates and the financing of research, and Intevep's legal status as a foundation. It gave the pros and cons of becoming a company, and concluded by asking PDVSA to consider transforming Intevep into a company. Humberto Calderon Berti, on October 27, made the presentation to the PDVSA Board and the presidents of the affiliates.

The October meeting with PDVSA was a milestone for Intevep and Calderon Berti, because it was resolved at this meeting that by-laws be prepared for Intevep, to become a mercantile company (Sociedad Anonima). And, Intevep was to prepare a plan of how it could participate in the development of new processes that the industry had contracted abroad for technical assistance. They were also to address: the duo-subordination of Intevep employees working at the installations of operating affiliates; and the question of responsibility for projects. And important to Intevep, it would have a representative at negotiations on technical assistance contracts (CATs). All of these matters were to be discussed at a follow-up meeting on December 8th, between PDVSA, the affiliates and Intevep.

Among the observations in the October 1978 report were two basic points. First, that Intevep not be overburdened with secondary activities, which distract it from its fundamental objectives. And second, that as Intevep changes from a foundation to a company that it not lose but rather maintain some tested organizational concepts. Oddly, there was only one example given of a concept that should not be lost — i.e., that they continue to have outside part-time directors from the affiliates (which, since 1986, Intevep no longer has). Even though Intevep has grown rapidly, it has managed not to become too overburdened with secondary activities and, therefore, the first point was carried out. On the second point, it is easy to see that Intevep is now run like an affiliate company.

Intevep's formal contacts with PDVSA and the operating affiliates was through the outside Directors, the Liaison Advisory Committee (Comite Asesor de Enlace), the committees of PDVSA and of the operators, and the Continuation of the Technical Assistance Contracts Committee.

Finally, the October report pointed out the need of clarification on how research should be charged. Intevep suggested prorating expenses for research that would be used by all or several of the operating affiliates; and charging only the operator who has an interest in a particular project; and having PDVSA finance larger and long term projects, which the operators do not have an immediate interest in, but which are considered necessary by PDVSA or Intevep.

In 1979, when Intevep became a company, its capital was subscribed at Bs. l million, with 100 shares at Bs. 10 thousand per share. PDVSA had 99 shares and Corpoven one share. Later, in increments, it rose, and by 1983, the statutes of Intevep were changed and the subscribed capital was raised to Bs. 700 million, with 700 shares and each share worth Bs. l million. With this change, PDVSA has all the shares.

Intevep changed from a simple foundation with: a Board of Directors, Executive Committee, with two Division Managers, three Technical Managers, and four Unit Supervisors, to a company power structure. There is now a controlled hierarchy with power descending from the **Assembly** (Asamblea), which somewhat resembles a stockholders meeting. The Assembly represents the owner (PDVSA) of Intevep, S.A., and meets in ordinary meetings (twice a year), or extraordinary meetings (when needed). The Intevep Board of Directors calls for the ordinary meeting and publishes a notice of the meeting in a daily newspaper. The extraordinary meeting is called by PDVSA (the stockholder), or the

Intevep Board. The Assembly names the Board of Directors, President and Vice President, determines their salaries, approves the Board's annual report and budget, authorizes programs and expansion of the company, determines end of the year bonuses (which under Venezuelan law are paid to all workers before Christmas), salaries, and retirements, etc..

Next in the hierarchy of power is the **Board of Directors**, which is the executive organ and *directs the administration* of Intevep. The Board is composed of five members, the President, Vice President, and three full time Directors, appointed for two years and can be re-elected. In addition to the Board, there is the **Executive Committee**, which is in charge of the daily activities of the company. This committee has the same members as the Board. There is the customary office of President and Vice President with responsibility for the daily operations of the company, and who preside at Board and Committee meetings (i.e., the Vice President in the absence of the President).

In 1988, PDVSA announced a new **double-track** or double career corporate ladder for **technical/scientist** and **administration/management**, so that Intevep's researchers could be recognized and rewarded by being classified for salary increases and promotions just as oilmen are. The double-track was necessary if Intevep was to retain its best researchers and attract new people. Departures of qualified researchers were increasing, because their skills were in demand in private industry where they could double or triple their salaries. According to the chart in Intevep's Organization Manual, a principal adviser in the technical/scientist track is on a par with a general manager, which appears to be where they hit the glass ceiling. Only one man has broken through.

Technical Services and Basic Engineering to Technological Support

I n 1988, another basic change in Intevep's organization occurred — Technical Services and Engineering were added to Intevep's corporate structure, and became the *Technology Division*. Peter Maurer came from Maraven, one of the three operating affiliates, to head the new division.

This change was a result of a PDVSA Executive Committee decision in October 1987, to create a central entity of technical services and engineering. The increasing demands in the Venezuelan petroleum industry for new technology and the need to have an efficient transfer of this technology, from its creation and development to its application and utilization, was the cause of this organizational change. The new system, called Organization Goal, was to be a turnkey transfer process — from development to transfer of the technology, i.e., an integrated process from conception to utilization within the Venezuelan industry. This meant that within Intevep the various research and technical groups would be working closely, and the engineering group, in turn, would be in close contact with their client operating company.

Patents

In order to protect, evaluate, *and* commercialize their industrial research results, Intevep, in 1987, formed the Appraisal of Technologies division. The number of patents a research center has received and has pending is one way of evaluating a center's credibility. In spite of its youth and necessary lead times, Intevep already has a remarkable record. Intevep has already received a number of important patents, particularly those related to the Orinoco Belt, as well as for refining processes. The total number of patents received from the United States, as of December 31, 1991, was *90*, of which they received 15 patents in both 1989 and 1990. The U.S. is one of the few countries that still awards patents to the inventors of the products, instead of the first parties to apply for such patents. Presently, there are negotiations between the U.S., Japan and the European Community that could lead to changes in international patent practices.

Intevep has applied for patents in a number of countries where PDVSA affiliates market their products, e.g., in: Canada, the United Kingdom, Brazil, France, Spain, Germany, Switzerland, Italy, Belgium, Japan, and Venezuela. Overall patents received as of the end of 1991, number 249, of which several were Lagoven's and Maraven's. And, Intevep had *434* patents still *pending*.

The following are the trademarks of Intevep's major discoveries, and the number of patents in each. They have five *U.S. patents* in **Imulsion** (heavy crudes technology); three patents in **Orimulsion** (heavy crudes product); five patents in **HDH** (refining process and catalyst); one patent in **HHC** (refining streams are improved by hydrocracking high resid); two in **Coflow** (core-annular flow process for very heavy viscous crudes); four in **INT-R1** (catalyst); three in **INT-FCC-1** (a cracking catalyst); three in **Forceliner** (a line of centering guides for downhole production equipment); and two in **VRS** (sucker rod centralizer - a solution for the gas/steam-lock problem in the production of heavy crudes). From these trademarks and patents, it is easy to see that Intevep's primary research has been in extra heavy oil and in their refining processes.

Among Intevep researchers, i.e., inventors, with their names on the most patents, **Dr. Roberto Galiasso**, with a Ph.D. from the University of Sciences of Paris, has over 20 U.S. patents — for HDH, HHC refining processes, and catalysts. On six of these patents, **Beatriz Arias**'s name also appears. Women researchers at Intevep have also been making a considerable contribution. Among these women are: **Maria Luisa Chirinos**, who has eight patents and worked on the Imulsion and Orimulsion discoveries and has degrees in Chemistry from the University of Birmingham, the U.K., and the University of Wisconsin, and is head of the Crude Handling Section; **Dr. Magdalena Ramirez de Agudelo**, with a Ph.D. in Chemistry from the University of Bath, the U.K., has 10 patents in catalysts, and is head of the Olefins Production Project; and **Carmen Galarraga,** who shares four of Dr. Agudelo's catalyst patents. (More on the Intevep women in the last chapter.)

Research on the HDH process was first started at IVIC, by **Julio Krasuk**, and later, Intevep senior scientist, whose name is on eight patents for processing heavy crudes. HDH is a deep conversion refining process for residual fuels, which offers higher flexibility for processing a variety of feedstocks.

As with HDH, the initial research on Orimulsion did not commence at Intevep, but began years earlier, in 1970, at Shell Oil in western Venezuela. The story, as told to the author by Nelson Vasquez, who at that time was with Shell, commenced with **Eli Schwartz** who went to Vasquez with the idea of field test burning heavy oil (Laguna) with 20% water. Later, Schwartz went to Intevep, followed by **Domingo Rodriguez**, and they started working on the process at Intevep.

Rodriguez has three U.S. patents on Orimulsion® and five on Imulsion®.

The first requested patents to protect this process technology were under *Imulsion*, in 1983 and 1984. Once Intevep/Lagoven achieved commercial technology, Intevep requested patents (1986-1989) for the entire manufacturing process under *Orimulsion*. With further research, production costs have declined, and the quality of Orimulsion has improved, e.g., the caloric content has risen and the viscosity declined. Today, Intevep has all of the important patents for emulsion technology in the world, according to Dr. Barroeta, Vice President of Intevep. (In 1991, Intevep purchased for $7 million, the licenses of Petroferm, Inc., a small Florida company that claimed to have developed a technology that could convert heavy crudes into a clean burning fuel. Petroferm obtained a patent in October 1986. Intevep's purchase eliminated a potential problem with Petroferm.)

In studying the list of patents, it is apparent that many of the inventors came from IVIC with Dr. Barroeta.

The inventors and researchers are the unsung heroes, the men and women that truly contribute. They are the foundation and the reason Intevep can be called a research center. Without them, there is no Intevep! The researchers and technicians remain the core of Intevep.

The Presidents and the Vice Presidents of Intevep

● **Humberto Calderon Berti**
The first president was the founding father of Invepet and of Intevep, serving at Intevep from January 1, 1976 to June 1979. Intevep's creation might not have succeeded but for the driving force of this man. His footsteps are on every page of its history.

● **Jose Martorano Battisti**
was the figurehead that General Alfonzo insisted be president of Intevep, thus denying Calderon Berti his rightful title.

● **Evanan Romero**
Evanan Romero was Calderon Berti's vice president, and he remained V.P. from January 1976 until April 1984, when he was transferred to the Board

of Meneven, one of the then four operating affiliates. He has a Masters in petroleum engineering from the University of Tulsa, and worked for Shell and Atlantic Refining in Venezuela. Romero is one of the founders of Invepet and Intevep. He told the author in an interview that these were the best years of his life.

● **Nelson Vasquez**

Mr. Vasquez became president when Intevep became a company. He served from June 1979 to August 1981, when he became a member of the Board of Directors of PDVSA. Mr. Vasquez worked for Shell in Venezuela and in 1976 became a member of the Board of Maraven, S.A., one of the four operating affiliates. Later, he was appointed manager of Maraven's western production division, until he became president of Intevep.

● **Armando Segnini**

Mr. Segnini was president from August 1981, until February 1985, when he became vice president of Lagoven, S.A., one of the four operating affiliates. Mr. Segnini told the author a story about his appointment. On Thursday he met with General Alfonzo for 10 minutes and was told he was to go to Intevep as President **on** Monday. He asked why? And was told by the General, "you are disciplined." But he was much more. He was "a client who went to learn about research and so I had to talk to everyone. I was so excited." Mr. Segnini was a visible and approachable president. He brought the heart of the oil industry to Intevep and embraced the "Intevep family." Mr. Segnini started working for Creole (Exxon) after he graduated from college and rose through different positions to be a member of the Lagoven Board, the position he held before he became president of Intevep.

● **Dr. Nestor Barroeta**

Dr. Barroeta became vice president in April 1984, and continues in that position. He and his group of researchers came from IVIC and were the core of scientists that made it possible to call Intevep a research institute. Dr. Barroeta has a Ph.D. in Chemistry from University College, London. Before becoming V.P. of Intevep, Dr. Barroeta was manager of the Refining and Petrochemical Division and a member of the Board. This chemist has been the continuing thread of good research, planning and development from the early days at Intevep up to the present.

The first three presidents, Calderon Berti, Vasquez and Segnini, have Masters degrees.

● **Gustavo Inciarte**

Mr. Inciarte, who was on the Board of Meneven, became president of Intevep, in February 1985, and continues in that position. Mr. Inciarte after receiving a B.S. in petroleum engineering from Oklahoma University joined Shell in Venezuela where he rose through the production operation of the company. He has been president of Intevep for the longest period, which has been a period of great growth. And, he saw a need for a book on Intevep's first 15 years, and asked the author to write it — with no map or directions given, but with open doors.

To be born and become strong comes first. During infancy we need support, and in manhood we shall have learned how to defend ourselves.

Simon Bolivar, The Liberator
Magdalena, February 17, 1826
Letter to Jose Rafael Revenga

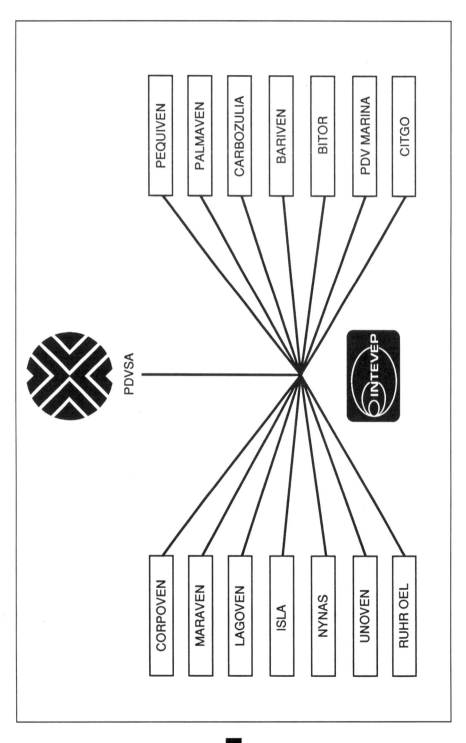

Greeting the President of Venezuela at Intevep's 15 year Anniversary Celebration in 1989. From left, Nestor Barroeta, Vice President, Intevep; Juan Chacin, President, PDVSA; Gustavo Inciarte, President, Intevep; Carlos Andres Perez, President of Venezuela.

From left, Nestor Barroeta, Vice President, Intevep; Not identified; Gustavo Inciarte, President, Intevep; Carlos Andres Perez, President of Venezuela: Alejandro Villoria.

From left, Armando Segnini, former President of Intevep; Humberto Calderon Berti, first President of Intevep; Alejandro Villoria, a Founder, Luis Herrera Campins, former President of Venezuela, General Rafael Alfonzo Ravard, first President of PDVSA.

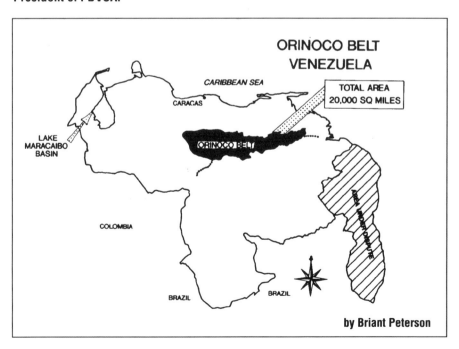

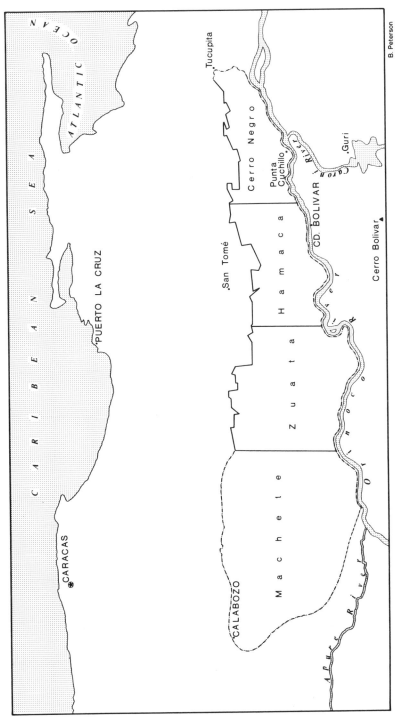

ORINOCO BELT

B. Peterson

CHAPTER V

THE ORINOCO BELT AND ORIMULSION

Oil and Water Do Mix

Venezuela's sleeping whale, the Orinoco Heavy Oil Belt, represents the largest natural oil spill in the world. With oil-in-place of some **1.2 trillion barrels**, there is no other continuous oil reserve that is so vast in the world. The Belt is roughly 20,000 square miles, with the outline of a whale on the map of Venezuela, and located along the north bank of the Orinoco River, Venezuela's major river. It is an irregular strip, 435 miles long by 31 to 62 miles wide — and lies between the towns of Calabozo, Guarico, in the west, and Tucupita, Orinoco Delta, in the east. The Belt covers parts of the states of Guarico, Anzoategui, Monagas, and the Delta Amacuro Federal Territory. The northern boundary of the Belt that pushes into the southern boundary of the old foreign oil concessions was the more difficult to determine. The southern boundary of the Belt parallels the banks of the Orinoco River.

Although its existence has been known since U.S. geologists explored the area in the late 1920s and early 1930s, the Oil Belt, formerly called the Tar Belt and now called the **Orinoco Belt**, is essentially untapped. Discoveries of lighter conventional oil in Venezuela continually discouraged the development of the Orinoco Belt. That has now changed.

After nationalization of the oil industry, PDVSA divided up the Belt among the then four operating companies and explored it to determine its size and the characteristics of its oil. After determining the vastness of the Belt in 1983, PDVSA was forced to postpone Lagoven's mega-project in Cerro Negro, because the decline of oil prices made the project uneconomic. However, the industry has used the intermittent years, with Intevep's help, to develop the technology to produce a new fuel (Orimulsion), a new way of transporting Orinoco oil (Core-Flow), and a process to upgrade it (HDH). Thus, when the market is ready for Orinoco oil, the Venezuelan oil industry will be ready to pick up speed and meet demand. Through Intevep, they have developed the technology!

The Belt contains a large number of reservoirs with oils that vary as to their properties and characteristics. The oil-bearing sands range in depth from 500 to 4,000 feet, in Tertiary Age unconsolidated, porous and highly permeable sands. The main producing areas in the Belt are from east to west: Cerro Negro, Pao, Hamaca, San Diego, Zuata, and Machete. Crude oils in the Belt are highly mobile inspite of their low API gravity, which ranges from 13 degrees in Cerro Negro to 3 degrees (bitumen) in Machete, with most of the reserve ranging between 8 and 11 degrees. The Orinoco Belt's other characteristics range from 2% to 5% sulfur content, 200 to 1,000 ppm vanadium, and 50 to 150 parts per million nickel.

Reservoir temperatures in the Belt are high (between 120 and 140 degrees F), which enables oil to flow under reservoir conditions. *Steam soak* is used in primary recovery to further increase recovery, and some day, *steam drive* technology will be used in secondary recovery. The steam injection method was **first used** in Venezuela by Shell, in 1957, in the Mene Grande field (one of the Bolivar Coastal fields), and is called "huff and puff". The method is efficient because the reservoirs are basically of a very unconsolidated nature. The result is low cost oil.

With steam soak, production rates from wells in the northern sections adjacent to the conventional oil fields range from 800 to 1,400 b/d.

Since transporting this heavy oil was difficult, the traditional way was to add diluents or higher gravity crude to make it flow through pipelines. Mene Grande started the process in its southern Anzoategui fields, and Meneven (now Corpoven) increased production using the same downhole method. To reduce surface equipment costs, the operating companies drilled wells in clusters in the Belt.

The Tar Belt and the Guayana Shield

The Orinoco Belt was called the "Tar Belt" for over 40 years. Geologists working for foreign oil companies like Gulf Oil and Standard had explored in the area in the late 1920s, and in the 1930s. After Standard of Venezuela (SOV) discovered Quiriquire in 1928, and started moving their rigs south in the state of Monagas, their geologists and engineers found enormous layers of sedimentary sands with heavy crudes with large sulfur contents, and high viscosity that made the oil difficult to produce and transport.

Prior to Gulf's and Standard's entrance into Eastern Venezuela in the 1920's, the Guanoco field under the asphalt lake, was discovered in 1913, and was under concession to the New York and Bermudez Company. Wells were drilled on the lake, but the oil they produced was nearly as heavy as the asphalt in the lake.

Standard came into Eastern Venezuela via the Gulf of Paria, up the San Juan River, and built their camp at Caripito, near their Quiriquire producing field. Gulf/Mene Grande, on the other hand, started from the Caribbean port city of Barcelona, in 1923, moving southward until they set up their headquarters in 1928, in Ciudad Bolivar, where the author's father was District Manager of Eastern Venezuela, until he built San Tome and it became the Mene Grande headquarters, in 1940. Mene Grande's exploration, therefore, went from Barcelona up to the Orinoco River, and therefore, right through the Tar Belt. Gene Brossard raised his children with his stories about "Venezuela's Black Ace-In-The-Hole." There was more oil in the Belt than Venezuela could ever produce. When the world ran out of light crude, Venezuela could supply as much heavy oil as they could use. Venezuela had an endless supply of heavy oil.

And why did exploration and drilling *stop* north of the Orinoco — why did it not continue into Venezuela's enormous Gran Sabana area? A great Precambrian landmass, called the **Guayana Shield** (Escudo de Guayana), is centered south of the Orinoco River. In 1928, a Gulf geologist was flying his Ford Tri-Motor plane down the Orinoco River and then swung south into the state of Bolivar, where the sun's reflection on the exposed minerals of a hill caught his eye, just as his instruments went wild. This large hill and smaller hills in the area "lie as natural magnets on a relatively non-magnetic granite shield, and they have such a strong pull as to attract a Brunton compass near these outcrops." (from the geological report of E. E. Brossard and J.T. Murrell, May 31, 1928, in the old Mene Grande Oil Co. files, under 193-A:8)

There were two discoveries made here, the iron mountain, Cerro Bolivar (Cerro Buenos Aires), and the northernmost corner of the exposed Guayana Shield! They were the oldest rocks in Venezuela. In a later geological report, in November 1931, on the small Pao Iron mines southeast of Ciudad Bolivar, Brossard included pages of photographs of iron ore hills in the area. After U.S. Steel, in need of new sources of iron ore after World War II, "discovered" Cerro Bolivar in 1947, the development of Venezuela's rich iron ore deposits got underway, and by the 1960s Venezuela's iron industry ranked second to its oil industry. Thus, south of the Orinoco River, the Granite Shield is exposed and this is the area of Venezuela's *iron ore* deposits and steel industry, *bauxite* deposits and aluminum industry (the largest producer in Latin America), *gold* mines, and *diamond* mines. This area also has great natural beauty, for it is where Angel Falls is located, as well as the expansive Gran Sabana, the incredible Sarijama depressions, and the cloud covered Roraima.

Gulf and Standard, which operated north of the Orinoco River, were aware of the Guayana Shield prior to the 1928 Brossard discovery. In a March 1927 detailed "Resume of Geology of Northeastern Venezuela," by E. E. Brossard and J. W. West, there are several references to igneous rocks *north* of the Orinoco River, as well as a description of two land masses in Eastern Venezuela.

A landmass off the north coast, the highest peaks of which may have been the present islands of Tortuga and Margarita. Another landmass occupied the present site of the **Guayana shield**. Sedimentation was rapid and variable, as this newly formed trough and its adjacent landmasses were not in a perfect state of equilibrium. (p. 8)

The sea advanced into this trough, or geosynclinal basin, between these two old landmasses, and Comanchean sediments began to form sedimentary rock. "Thus, we find massive fossiliferous limestones underlain and overlain by thick coarse grained fossiliferous sandstones." (p. 54)

One of the early geological reports on the Guayana Shield was done in 1938, by Augustine (Gus) Pyre, a Gulf geologist. Mr. Pyre worked in the Oficina laboratory of Mene Grande with Dr. Hollis Hedberg. Using cores of basement rocks from 17 southern Anzoategui and southern Monagas wells, Pyre studied the unconformity between the basement and overlying sediments, and the data on the amount of weathering of the basement. The basement that Pyre found in southern Anzoategui and southern Monagas, i.e., wells in the Belt, was the northern dip of the Guayana Shield. "The most abundant rocks are granitic gneisses." (p. 2) Interestingly, Pyre writes that "the only definitely sedimentary rock encountered is the phyllite from La Canoa No. 1," a well which had been drilled in 1935, by Standard. "All of the other rocks are quite typical of the gneissic complex which makes up the greater part of the shield." (p. 3) These 17 wells in Anzoategui and Monagas, studied for their basement rocks, stretched from Algarrobo-Yopales to Temblador in the east. Among the 17 wells studied, the most southerly were: Pilon No. 1, Cerro Negro No. 1, and Canoa No. 1. Pyre found that "the strike lines of the old surface, like the regional structure of the Guayana shield, nearly parallel the course of the Orinoco." (p. 4)

Besides establishing the Guayana Shield as the basement for the wells drilled in southern Anzoategui and Monagas, Gus Pyre's report is important for noting the gentler dip of the basement surface between the Orinoco River and these 17 southerly wells, *and* between the 17 wells *and* other wells further north in the basin. Between the Orinoco River and La Canoa No. 1 the dip is about 60 feet/km, whereas from La Canoa northward, the dip is about 100 feet/per kilometer. (p.4) From this, it is clear that the Orinoco Belt becomes more prolific as you move north and away from the Orinoco River and away from the surfaced Guayana Shield.

In the competitive world in which we now live, which makes company reports proprietary and secretive, the oil industry in Venezuela functioned and functions differently. The companies in Venezuela were friendly and they shared information about the country. When Buck Nolan sent the Pyre report to Chester Crebbs, the president of Mene Grande in Caracas, he also sent a copy to Henry Linam, who was the president of Standard Oil of Venezuela, in Quiriquire. He could not do otherwise, for Standard had shared its cores of basement rocks with Mene Grande.

By the late 1930s, the foreign oil companies understood that the oil in the Tar Belt was not commercial, and would have to wait for a later date to be produced. They could not really transport it, and their overseas refineries could not refine it. Therefore, they concentrated on their concessions to the north, as they built their infra-structure of roads, oil camps, and pipelines, etc.. However, some heavy oil from the Belt was produced. Standard brought in the big Temblador field in the Maturin basin in 1936, and in 1958, the Morichal field, north of the Cerro Negro area, was discovered by Amoco. And Mene Grande after bringing in the big Oficina field in 1937, used to dilute heavier crudes from its southern concession area with lighter Oficina crude to market a $17°$ API gravity crude. Meneven continued to do this and in 1980 was producing 66,000 b/d of heavy or extra heavy oil and mixing it with the lighter Oficina oil.

Early Estimates of the Belt

The first estimate of oil-in-place in the Orinoco Belt was presented in April **1967**, to the 7th World Petroleum Congress, in Mexico, by Jose Galavis, a geologist with the Ministry, and Hugo Velarde, a geologist with CVP. The regional study, using scout-well data available on the existing geological and geophysical records, was the task of Corporacion Venezolana del Petroleo (CVP), started in April 1965 and completed in February 1966. They designated four principal areas of petroleum concentrations, from east to west: Machete, Zuata, Hamaca, and Cerro Negro. At the time they estimated the oil-in-place as about 700 billion barrels of heavy oil. Another study, "The Orinoco Oil Belt," made in 1976, by Francisco J. Gutierrez, Oil Belt Director in the Ministry, gives no estimate, but in another report the following year he estimated the oil-in-place as exceeding 2 trillion barrels. An intensive exploration program was obviously needed to determine Venezuela's reserves in the Orinoco Belt.

In 1968, M. Stephenson completed another study of geological data on the Belt, for the Ministry of Mines and Hydrocarbons. And the same year, the Ministry asked IVIC to conduct some laboratory and field work on the Belt's hydrocarbons; and the Ministry asked CVP to start drilling stratigraphic wells and shoot the first 1000 kilometers of seismic lines. Over the next five years the program was expanded, and an Office for the Belt was formed within the Ministry. This effort by IVIC and CVP showed that the sedimentary section was thicker, and that the hydrocarbon area extended further to the south — closer to the Orinoco River than had previously been thought.

The Tar Belt has gone through a number of name changes. After the first *preliminary evaluation* of the potential resources of the Belt — done between 1965 and 1966 by CVP — the name went from Tar to Heavy Oil. And after the conclusion of the successful exploratory program started by PDVSA in 1979 and concluding in 1983, with oil-in-place determined to be 1.2 trillion barrels, the name became the Orinoco Oil Belt. In 1990, for political/economic reasons the name settled down to two words: **Orinoco Belt**. In Venezuela, the common name used for years is simply, **La Faja**.

PDVSA Gets the Orinoco Belt

A t the time of nationalization in 1975, the Ministry of Mines and Hydrocarbons had all the legal tools for almost complete oil-industry control. In November 1971, President Rafael Caldera issued **Decree 832**, which was intended to clarify and regulate the provisions of the Law of Reversion of 1971. Foreign oil companies were now required to submit in October of each year, a copy of their operational programs *for the approval* of the Ministry prior to their execution. Ministry bureaucrats became the managers of the oil industry, and the Director of the new Reversion Division was Calderon Berti! There were other competing divisions within the Ministry, particularly the Hydrocarbons Division. Rivalry was strong, and the oil companies were often caught in-between division chiefs within the Ministry vying for turf and power.

After the January 1, 1976 departure of the foreign oil companies, the Ministry staff argued that Decree 832 was still in force and they would run PDVSA and the affiliates the way they had the foreign oil companies. PDVSA argued that **it** had been created to coordinate and control the activities of the oil industry, so as to fulfill the basic objectives of its shareholders (the nation). The basic source of this problem was mistrust. Ministry officials did not trust the managerial group heading the new national oil industry because they had been trained by and worked for the multinationals. When it came to *exploration*, the head of the Hydrocarbons Division, Arevalo Guzman Reyes (later a Board member of PDVSA) said that exploration in new areas should be done by the Ministry. Calderon Berti objected and supported the industry.

The deep differences between the Ministry and PDVSA over exploration were brought to a head over the Orinoco Belt. The Venezuelan newspapers, on February 7, 1976, reported that Minister Valentin Hernandez said there was a possibility of negotiating pilot projects in the Belt with the governments of Canada and Rumania and with some U.S. multinationals. This was barely a month *after* the industry had been nationalized. Actually, Minister Hernandez preferred handing the Orinoco Belt project over to PDVSA, but his staff was not in favor. They preferred outside contractors. There was already a small Oil Belt Office in the Ministry, which Francisco J. Gutierrez headed.

PDVSA went to President Carlos Andres Perez and requested a decision. In their memorandum to the President, PDVSA stressed the similarities between Orinoco heavy oil reservoirs and the areas they were already operating in, nearby, in Morichal, Jobo, and Pilon oil fields. *And*, the research and experimental needs of the project could be better handled by *Intevep*, than by outside contractors. Thus, Intevep was one of the arguments used by PDVSA to get the Oil Belt.

In *December 1977*, the Perez government assigned the Orinoco Oil Belt to Petroleos de Venezuela; and PDVSA, after marking out four sectors, assigned each of the four operating affiliates a region, in **September 1978**. Each affiliate was responsible for the exploration and development planning of its region.

In 1979, Petroleos de Venezuela initiated an intensive exploration program to delineate and quantify hydrocarbon resources in the Orinoco Belt, by 1983. The program was described as a *reconnaissance effort* to confirm expected enormous amounts of heavy oil-in-place. From this study, not only would the unknown reserves be determined, the most prospective areas for exploitation would be selected.

Because the area was so extensive, the 20,000 square miles (54,000 sq kilometers) was divided, unevenly, between the then four operating affiliates. Corpoven got the largest area, in the west, named **Machete**, Maraven got **Zuata**, Meneven was given **Hamaca**, and finally in the east, Lagoven got the smallest but geologically better **Cerro Negro**.

Meneven and **Lagoven** had operated in their sectors since the 1920s, when their predecessor companies were Mene Grande (Gulf) and Standard (later Creole). They already had explored the area and had near-by production **and** infra-structure. As a result, these two affiliates were assigned the first *production* under PDVSA's new Oil Belt program.

The other two affiliates, i.e., **Corpoven** and **Maravem**, were assigned *general exploration* of their areas: evaluation of the existing accu-mulations of hydrocarbons; evaluation of other existing energy resources and aquifers; and the evaluation of the feasibility of the development and exploitation of the oil reservoirs found. They carried out seismographic surveys to determine the subsurface configuration, and they drilled around 328 wildcat wells, between 1980 and 1982.

Maraven was the company with the most historical experience with heavy oil production, for when it had been Shell de Venezuela, it had been **the** pioneer. In 1957, for the first time anywhere, Shell started using steam injection in their Mene Grande field, in the Bolivar Coastal fields of Lake Maracaibo. Out of the 200 wells that Maraven drilled in its assigned **Zuata** area in the Belt, they found potential production ranging from 20 to 300 b/d with an average of crude oils of 10 degrees API. Maraven's Zuata sector is 40% in the state of Guarico, and 60% in the state of Anzoategui, where south of Pariaguan they found, in a smaller area, crude oil with a gravity from $15°$ to $20°$ API. Maraven also found isolated layers of coal, two to four feet thick.

Corpoven also had experience with heavy oil, for in Western Venezuela, in Zulia, they produce extra-heavy crude at Campo Boscan. And Corpoven operates fields of heavy crude oils along the northern mar-gin of the Belt. In Melones, they had been experimenting with in situ combustion. Corpoven's **Machete** sector of the Belt is entirely in the state of Guarico. Besides running seismic lines and drilling wells, etc., Corpoven in Guarico had to build roads, bridges, and the infra-structure in an area of scant population. In doing so, Corpoven, as the other three companies also did, took special care to select the most adequate areas for opening up roads, in order to avoid damaging the ecology of the area. And after the exploratory period was completed, forestation and sanitation programs were carried out. The new roads, of course, made a considerable contribution to the state highway system, just as the roads that the foreign concessionaires had built when they operated in Venezuela — helping to open up the country.

Development was to take place in the next two sectors of the Belt, i.e., within **Hamaca** and **Cerro Negro**. Areas *within* these two sectors were to be developed, and were selected as the most promising because they had an infra-structure nearby. Thus, while oil has been found in commercial quantities in all areas of the Belt, priority status was given to the Lagoven and Meneven areas only, in order to plan an orderly development in the areas (covering about 8% of the Belt) that would permit the greatest return on investment, while allowing time for future technological breakthroughs. **Intevep** now had the largest laboratory in the world — the Belt!

PDVSA completed the evaluation of the Belt in **five intensive years**: drilling 662 wells, of which 546 were successful (83%), processing 16,000 miles of seismic lines, gravimetric, magnetometric and aeromagnetic studies. The cost of the exploration effort was **$615 million**, and the final count on the crude oil in the Orinoco Belt was announced on March 1, 1984, i.e., 1.2 trillion barrels of oil in-place. Assuming a recovery factor of 22%, the reserves were estimated at 267 billion barrels, which would enable Venezuela to produce 2 million b/d for 500 years!

But knowing that you have this enormous reserve of heavy oil, and producing it, are not synonymous. Long lead times to develop Orinoco oil are necessary — first the technology and then the infra-structure, or it could be the reverse depending on the region of the Belt. After years of intense work on the part of the four operating companies, and with a mega-project (DSMA) in the planning for Lagoven, PDVSA was forced in December 1982, to *scale down* its Orinoco Belt program.

Venezuela's Foreign Debt

 n event that historically can be called a pillage, and which affected the development of the Orinoco Belt, was the October 27, 1982 transfer of PDVSA's $3.7 billion foreign funds to the Central Bank of Venezuela. General Alfonzo at a meeting with U.S. reporters in

August 1983, said that PDVSA would suffer a 20% reduction in net profits in 1983, because of the loss of control of its foreign cash reserves. (*Oil Daily*, 8/29/83, p.A-6) According to the PDVSA annual report, those reserves earned an average 14.3%, in 1982. The General said that at the end of 1981, PDVSA had about $6 billion in banks around the world.

The newspaper, *El Diario de Caracas*, on November 4, 1982, in an article on the subject, quoted a PDVSA executive as saying "we have been victims of a *golpe de Estado.*" The article continues: "PDVSA created the fund with the purpose of using it to explore and develop the Orinoco Oil Belt." In 1983, PDVSA had its first cash flow problems, a result of declining international oil demand, due to a world wide recession and its OPEC quotas, plus its loss of foreign exchange holdings, and its subsidization of domestic gasoline prices. The first budget cuts were in heavy oil development!

Orinoco Belt Projects Are Planned, Then Put on Hold

When PDVSA obtained administrative control of the Belt, it created a coordinating office and established a Master Plan to conduct an evaluation of the whole area. Besides the general exploration to obtain better knowledge of the distribution and quality of the crudes in the Belt, PDVSA wanted to evaluate the upgrading technologies available in order to utilize the most promising. All of this was for the purpose of developing a production program to obtain about 600,000 b/d by 1995, and 1 million b/d by 2000.

The largest target of development for this program was to be Lagoven's Cerro Negro sector: 125,000 b/d by 1988, and about 500,000 b/d by 2000. The second development program was Meneven's Guanipa project, in the Hamaca sector, to produce 100,000 b/d by 1988. These two projects were to add a total of 225,000 b/d to Venezuela's production, by 1988.

Known as the **DSMA project** (Desarrollo Sur Monagas y Anzoategui), Lagoven was to develop a commercial project for the *production, upgrading* and *transportation* of some 125,000 b/d from **South Monagas and Anzoategui.** The project's design was to include eventual expansion of operations to 500,000 b/d. The Cerro Negro sector was close to Lagoven's producing fields, which Creole, Phillips and Amoco (both obtained large concessions in 1956-57) had been operating prior to nationalization. Thus, Lagoven had considerable data and operating experience in the area. Nevertheless, the project assigned to Lagoven was *enormous*, as Guillermo Rodriguez Eraso, President of Lagoven at the time, explained in a long interview in 1981, for the Venezuelan magazine *Resumen*. Lagoven, which accounted for 45% of Venezuela's oil production, had just granted a contract to the U.S. engineering firm of C-E Lummus (and its Venezuelan partners) to act as the General Coordinator of Implementation. The contract was supposedly for eight years and $700 million. This came after a planning study that took two intensive years, and cost 300 to 350 million bolivars. Bechtel assisted the Lagoven technical advisers' team in preparing the Master Plan and budget estimates required to obtain PDVSA's approval, for what Rodriguez Eraso called "a megaproject." Industry sources said the overall project could cost $8 billion, by 1990.

For the *planning study*, Lagoven hired the services of national universities, signed contracts with *Intevep* and IVIC, gave the soil and agricultural studies to the University of the East (Oriente), and the study of the social and economic impact was done by Simon Bolivar University. The Lagoven project was in the middle of the southern Monagas savannah (Llanos), where there is nothing except the town of Temblador. It would be necessary to provide the people who were going to live near the project with an infra-structure and services. Rodriguez Eraso explained: "the Belt was going to provide an extremely valuable element, around which a real structure for national services to the oil industry could be developed." It would be the development of something immense, taking two or three decades. The Belt could be "a deeper nationalization," the sowing of oil, by rendering services to the oil industry and not sowing it in things that do not bear fruit.

Lagoven's megaproject in the Orinoco Belt was divided into a number of related projects. *Two pilot projects*: one in Jobo and the other in Cerro Negro proper, using steam injection, were built to evaluate reservoir behavior, optimum rates of production and injection and economic feasibility. To achieve the 125,000 b/d would require *drilling 1,000 wells* (Lagoven takes less than 5 days to drill a well in the Belt), and the construction of surface installations, and steam-injection plants. The most expensive and complex project would have been the *crude oil upgrading plant*, consisting of two parallel plants for distillation, delayed coking and hydrogeneration. It would need an electric power plant with a generating capacity of around 300 megawatts.

Because crude oils in the Belt are very deficient in hydrogen, i.e., they have a very low hydro-carbon ratio, the upgrading of these crude oils is basically to increase that ratio. The primary upgrading process is to convert the crude oil from South Monagas into a higher quality crude with low sulfur, metal, and carbon content.

Meneven's **Guanipa 100+ project** to increase heavy crude production to 100,000 b/d in southern Anzoategui was to use the existing installations to their maximum. For some 40 years, Mene Grande/Meneven used light oil to produce heavy oil by blending the two in the wellbore, and thus, recovered more than 250 million barrels through this method. About one barrel of 24 API gravity oil is needed to produce one barrel of 10° API gravity oil, resulting in two barrels of 17° API blended oil. This is not a very satisfactory way to produce Orinoco oil because you have to reduce the value of your higher grade oil to produce the heavy oil. New research at Intevep and in the field would make it easier and cheaper to produce this oil.

The Meneven area, in the Hamaca sector, is known as the Mesa de Guanipa, with blowing tall grasses and small stunted trees. The Guanipa 100+ project is just south of Meneven's traditional oil fields (Oficina, Merey, Ostra, Oveja, Oleos, Melones, etc.) and is geologically a continuation of those fields. This new production would be diluted with lighter oils to obtain a 17° API gravity oil, which can be refined in the Meneven (now Corpoven) refinery in Puerto La Cruz. Meneven also planned to run new seismic lines, drill around 300 exploration wells to define the areas of better hydrocarbon content, and drill between 1,300 to 1,800 production wells, construct new facilities, steam injection plants, etc.. In 1981 dollars, the Guanipa 100+ project was estimated at $1.32 billion.

Mene Grande and its successor Meneven had drilled, by 1983, more than 6,500 wells in Eastern Venezuela and produced more than 4.5 billion barrels in Anzoategui. However, in the 1980s, in the interest of encouraging agricultural development in the Mesa de Guanipa, in view of Venezuela's mounting food import bill, directional wells were to be drilled from a pad. A single cluster of 17 wells would require only 11 acres instead of the usual

77 acres. It would also save about $70,000 per well in gathering lines, electrical lines, insulated steam lines and ancillary equipment.

The environment was closely observed in the planning of the Belt's projects. In 1977, Marco Negron, an architect, published a study, "Prediagnosis for a Comprehensive Development Plan for the Orinoco Oil Belt." This and other discussions led to the drawing up of a *Land Management Plan*, which was agreed to by PDVSA and the Ministry of the Environment and National Renewable Resources, on June 10, 1980. About the size of Denmark, the Belt is in an area where most of the soils are not capable of sustaining commercial agriculture or cattle grazing. It is in the Llanos, or plains, with a dry season and a 6-month rainy season when it is hard to move rigs and equipment.

Intevep was to study the environmental impact of the development of the Belt. The study was to serve as a guide for decision making for the adoption of a master plan containing all the control measures for a balance between the development of the oil industry in the Belt, and the preservation of natural resources and compliance with the provisions of the Organic Law of the Environment.

However, with an excess of world oil supply over demand in 1981 and 1982, OPEC for the first time, in March 1982, set a limit to its total output and allocated individual production shares. In cutting back its production, Venezuela began to supplement heavier crude (with a lower price) with lighter crudes, and did more infill drilling. They moved three compression plants to Lagunillas and Tia Juana in the West, in order to increase production in these large producing fields, while they cut back elsewhere in Venezuela.

And, in December 1982, both Lagoven's and Meneven's projects went under re-evaluation by PDVSA and both companies had to scale back their projects. PDVSA announced that the new pace of development would concentrate on *pilot projects* in the Belt, rather than on immediate commercial development. As it turned out, this became Intevep's big opportunity.

Earlier in 1982, Venezuela had hosted in Caracas, the 2nd UNITAR Conference on Heavy Crudes and Tar Sands. It was the occasion for many papers presented by the Venezuelan oilmen on the successful exploration of the Orinoco Oil Belt. PDVSA had an 80% success rate in its drilling program, plus the relative ease with which wells can be drilled made the whole exercise in the Belt very promising. Their only real problem had been the six-month rainy season, which caused delays in moving rigs and equipment. Over 420 different zones were studied. The future looked bright for the development of the Belt at the UNITAR Conference, in February 1982.

With PDVSA's re-evaluation, the biggest, most expensive project was cut way back. Lagoven's Cerro Negro project was reduced to 35,000 b/d production of heavy crude, while Meneven's Guanipa-100 project still aimed for 100,000 b/d by 1988.

A project outside the Belt, the proposed $1 billion Nurgas natural gas pipeline, from Eastern Venezuela to Western Venezuela, was to go forward. This gas pipeline was necessary because of the poor shape of the old gas line, as well as projected increased gas demand, and the need for gas in Zulia to avoid sporadic gas shortages caused by crude production restrictions (OPEC). Thus, the system's capacity was insufficient and required a significant increase, along with a need to extend gas transmission to Western Venezuela. PDVSA also continued the building of the large Meneven Cryogenic Complex, on the coast, at Jose, Anzoategui, inaugurated in November 1985.

In 1982, PDVSA was also developing a new policy of "internationalization," investing in overseas refineries and securing downstream marketing facilities. The company became very concerned with its vulnerable outlet position, because of its lack of such facilities in consuming countries.

PDVSA had been studying the U. S. and European markets and they found an outlet in Europe for 100,000 b/d of extra-heavy crude. In December 1982, Veba Oel AG, a German state-controlled energy company, said it agreed with PDVSA to refine Venezuelan oil in two of its West German refineries. Ruhr Oel, a joint venture between PDVSA and Veba, was set up in 1983, with each company owning 50 percent. Venezuela was not only able to sell additional heavy oil, but at the same time was to gain new technology in upgrading heavy crudes.

One of the big losers in the downscaling of the Orinoco Belt projects was Combustion Engineering's Lummus, which had won the big contract from Lagoven. No final contract for actual construction had been signed, as Lummus and its Venezuelan firm Vepica were still working on preliminary designs of the upgrading plant, which was to process 170,000 b/d into 140,000 b/d of 32° API gravity feedstock with no residual cut. In May 1983, Lagoven formally notified Lummus that it had cancelled plans for its Cerro Negro project. During the two years that Lummus had worked on the designs, it had provided training for more than 200 Venezuelan engineers, on all aspects of engineering, procurement and project management, and for this, Lummus was reimbursed by Lagoven.

Lagoven had adopted delayed coking, followed by hydrotreating in its $2 billion upgrading plant that would have removed the Orinoco oil's sulfur and metal impurities. The postponement of the Cerro Negro project meant that Lagoven would start with primary recovery and move into enhanced recovery techniques.

The postponement gave PDVSA time to evaluate upgrading methods, *and* it gave Intevep time to concentrate its research on the Orinoco Belt and prove that it could invent and develop the needed technology to produce and market Orinoco oil. The patents and trademarks that Intevep has been granted prove its success in this research, principally Orimulsion, HDH and Core-Annular Flow!

Orimulsion®

So what if a fuel could be invented that could flow at a relatively low temperature, yet not be crude; burn very well, yet not be coal; and be more widely available and conceivably cheaper than either. *Energy Economist*, March 1988, p.14

Orimulsion is the registered trade name given to an emulsion of Orinoco® bitumen (natural bitumen) in water and stabilized by a specially formulated additive package. After the bitumen is produced, it goes through degasification, dehydration and desalting, and this raw material is then ready for the manufacturing process of forming an emulsion of Orinoco bitumen (70%) in water (30%).

The main constituent of this package is a surfactant belonging to the phenol ethoxylate group of compounds. The effectiveness of the surfactant and the quality of the final product are greatly influenced by other chemicals present in the package. (*Orimulsion, User Manual*, Bitor, January 1989, p.2/1)

The surfactants, known as emulsifying agents, are added to promote the stability of the emulsion. They form a molecular film that acts as a mechanical barrier preventing the droplets from coalescing.

Simply stated, Orimulsion® is a new liquid fuel in which water and a surfactant (INTAM-100) has been added to Orinoco® bitumen, which turns it into an emulsion with a viscosity resembling No. 6 heavy fuel oil (HFO), or even lower. The 70% Orinoco® bitumen component is between 7.5° and 9.5° API gravity, with sulfur content of 3.5 to 4% weight, and in metal content, vanadium is from 400 to 500 ppm, nickel 95 to 120 ppm, and iron 11 to 25 parts per million. By adding 30% water, the same impurities in Orimulsion are reduced and sulfur content is 2.4 to 2.9%, vanadium drops to 280 - 360 ppm, nickel to 66 - 86 ppm, and iron to 7 - 18 parts per million. (*Orimulsion User Manual*, Table 2.1, and Table 2.2)

One of the most important factors of Orimulsion® is the small size of the bitumen droplets in the emulsion, which must be evenly distributed in the water. The small evenly distributed droplets is a key factor that allows Orimulsion® to achieve its high combustion efficiency rate of 99.9 percent. An emulsion is basically a mixture of two immiscible liquids, one of which is dispersed in the other in the form of fine droplets. There are two types of emulsions, i.e., oil-in-water, which is what Orimulsion® is; and water-in-oil emulsions.

Orimulsion® is a new fuel for use by power utilities and heavy industry. Orimulsion® can be utilized in any oil-fired power station, with suitable pre-conditioning of the handling systems involving pipes, tanks, and burners. Orimulsion's possible drawback is the high sulfur content, therefore, for continuous use of the fuel a utility or company must install flue gas de-sulfurization equipment, in order to comply with permitted emission levels in most countries.

Orimulsion® would obviously be a competitor with coal in electric power generation. Natural gas would not be a competitor because it is so much cleaner to burn and prices are still low. But Orimulsion® could back out existing heavy fuel oil (HFO) consumption. "Given the ease of transfer from HFO burning to Orimulsion burning, power companies are not going to switch coal-fired capacity to the new fuel, when the job is more simply done by backing out HFO," wrote the *Energy Economist* of the Financial Times Business Information, in an article on "Bitumen emulsion," in March 1988.

It is for Bitor, S.A, PDVSA's new affiliate, to handle the job of exporting and finding markets for Orimulsion®. They offer *long term contracts* of 15 to 20 years, with the price adjusted with any changes in the price levels of steam coal. Orimulsion® is, thus, *attractively priced* below oil prices.

The Imulsion® technology is the result of some of the research that was conducted during a **1981** three-year Collaborative Research Agreement, between Intevep (signed by Armando Segnini, then president) and BP Research International. The purpose of the collaborative research agreement was to find an alternative and more economical method of producing and transporting heavy, extra-heavy crudes and bitumens, other than by using heat or adding expensive diluents to reduce the viscosity. British Petroleum had a special interest, because BP Canada was the operator of the heavy oil Wolf Lake project in Alberta, and it was using gas condensate as a diluent to transport its blend of heavy oil some 2,500 km to refineries in the U. S. Northern Tier.

Intevep and British Petroleum conducted research during the initial phase at BP's Research Centre (founded by Anglo Persian in 1922) in Sunbury, near London, and at Intevep's laboratories. During the first two years, they looked at the fundamental scientific behavior of emulsions and how to formulate them, using surfactants. In 1983-1984, Intevep and BP found that by mixing varying ratios of oil and the surfactant solution, which reduces the surface tension between the oil and water, a stable oil-in-water emulsion (where the two components do not separate) was achieved. A two-stage mixing process was required. First, a mixture of 90% bitumen and 10% water was emulsified, next, more water was added and mixed in (30% water to 70% bitumen) until the oil droplets assumed a spherical shape and remained evenly distributed and stable without any separation. After the two formation stages, the viscosity of the emulsion is reduced by three to four times, allowing it to flow with much greater ease compared with the original bitumen, thus solving the problem of transporting heavy oil/bitumen.

The jointly developed laboratory and pilot plant results were then expanded to the field, *independently*, by Intevep in Venezuela, and by BP in Canada, in 1985. This effort resulted in Intevep's Imulsion® technology, and BP's Transoil™.

During 1985, independently of one another, Intevep and BP discovered that these *emulsions* not only *flow easily* in a pipeline, they *also burn very well* in boilers and heaters. The Intevep Combustion Group, another research group, had been working on burning extra-heavy crudes as a fuel for production operations in the industry. Using steam injection to produce this oil, they then used some of the oil to produce steam in the oil fields. Small-scale tests on burning Orinoco® bitumen as a fuel were carried out in Venezuela in 1984, and in the Netherlands. Why not apply these combustion qualities of Orimulsion® for use as a burner fuel in power plants? The two Intevep research groups began working together in 1985, and conducted their first pilot-scale test at Intevep, in **July 1985**. Then, they joined forces with Lagoven!

While Intevep and Lagoven are responsible for the development of Orimulsion®, the first suggestion for *burning* heavy oil with water was Eli Schwartz's, when he was an engineer with *Shell* in Western Venezuela. In 1970, Schwartz went to Nelson Vasquez, Shell's chief engineer (and later president of Intevep), and suggested field test burning oil with 20% water, using Laguna oil. After Intevep was formed, Vasquez convinced Schwartz to go to Intevep, where he headed General Engineering, and he in turn recommended Roberto Rodriguez, who arrived when Vasquez went to Intevep as President. Schwartz and Rodriguez started the heavy oil section in General Engineering. According to Nelson Vasquez, it was Eli Schwartz who built the labs at Intevep where the first emulsion of heavy crude oil in water was prepared, in November 1979. And it was Schwartz who sent Ignacio Layrisse to BP in Sunbury, during the initial phase of research.

There was another precursor to Imulsion®, at *Creole*. According to the former President of Lagoven, Renato Urdaneta, Creole made *asphalt emulsions* at Amuay, in 1967. These asphalt emulsions were poured on roads in Europe and in the United States. Therefore, in 1985, as Lagoven joined forces with Intevep to study a means of producing Orinoco® bitumen from their Cerro Negro sector of the Belt, there were already precedents established by Shell and Creole (Exxon) men — and these pioneers would now be working together.

Mitsubishi made a proposal to Lagoven as early as 1984, to purchase Orinoco bitumen to burn in power plants in Japan. However, at the time, sea transportation of the bitumen was restricted to heated tankers of reduced size, thereby increasing overall costs, and the offer was thus not considered attractive.

Manuel de Oliveira, now president of BP Bitor, worked on the Lagoven program and was responsible for their **Orinoco Project** study. With the Cerro Negro mega-project canceled, Lagoven thought their solution to using the Belt was to burn Orinoco® emulsion as combustion. The Lagoven planning group with Joaquin Tredinick, now President of Bitor, Vicente Llatas, later the first vice president of Bitor, and Oliveira went to Intevep for help, seeking a way to burn directly.

At Intevep, Domingo Rodriguez, who already was working on combustion of bitumens within the Venezuelan-German Agreememt (1980-1984), started working on a plan to use Orinoco® bitumen as a boiler fuel for electric utilities. And in the emulsion group, Ignacio Layrisse along with Hercilio Rivas and Maria Luisa Chirinos were working on emulsification of bitumen for pipeline transportation. The combustion and emulsion groups now started to work together, and once the viability of fuel emulsion was established the project's efforts were concentrated on emulsions.

The more modest effort that started between Intevep and BP, now switched gears and became a driving force between Intevep and Lagoven, for the development of a new technology.

After Lagoven's Cerro Negro mega-project was canceled in 1983, Lagoven in 1984, set up two experimental production blocks — *J-20* and *O-16* — in the area near the town of Morichal. And in May 1985, when Jack Tarbes was president, Lagoven set up the Orinoco Project group to evaluate the market opportunities for Orimulsion® as a power station fuel. In September 1986, Lagoven began developing production capacity for Orimulsion® on the two production blocks, to enable fuel demonstration and evaluation of Intevep's new technology.

Intevep's Imulsion® technology had by now greatly changed from what it discovered when it was working with BP. A new name — *Orimulsion* — was coined by Domingo Rodriguez for the emulsified Orinoco® bitumen.

Lagoven wanted to market Orimulsion® as soon as possible. (Shiploading is currently from Punta Cuchillo Terminal on the Orinoco River. Later, Puerto La Cruz, which is a deepwater Caribbean terminal, will be used.) As they were opposed in doing so by the Ministry, particularly by Ulises Ramirez, Lagoven wanted to create its own company to market this new fuel that was not under OPEC quotas. Maraven and Corpoven, however, wanted a piece of the action, and so, Bitor, S.A. was created by PDVSA (but was not recognized by the Ministry, until now). In *7 plus years*, Orimulsion® went to market!

Combustion tests on Orimulsion® were performed to establish its application in steam generation, in electric power plants. After Intevep confirmed the combustibility of Orimulsion® in the laboratory and from a pilot plant, agreements were signed with Canadian, Japanese, British, and U.S. electric power companies to test Orimulsion® on a commercial scale.

The first cargo of Orimulsion® was shipped in **May 1988**, to Japan. There was no deterioration in the product from the 40-day ocean voyage of the 31,000 barrels of Orimulsion®, which was successfully tested at Chubu Electric Company in Nagoya, Japan. Other industrial scale trials of Orimulsion® completed during 1988-1989, were at: Babcock Energy Centre in Renfrew, Scotland; CEGB (PowerGen) in England; Aalborg Portland Cement-Fabrik in Denmark; and New Brunswick Power's Dalhousie in Canada. And in the United States, Florida Power & Light started testing 220,000 tons of Orimulsion® at one of its power plants, in 1991.

Orimulsion® is now established as a non-conventional fuel that can be burned in power plants, as an alternative to coal and high sulfur fuels. It can be delivered to international markets in conventional oil tankers. And it is a fuel with high combustion efficiency, high heating value, and a very stable clean burning flame. Furthermore, Orimulsion® has an unlimited supply of feedstock — the hundreds of billions of barrels of Orinoco oil/bitumen!

Because of this enormous potential, PDVSA formed a new affiliate, **Bitumenes Orinoco S.A. (BITOR)**, in *October 1988*, for the purpose of contracting with Lagoven and the other two affiliates, and of developing and marketing the bitumen resources from the Orinoco Belt. In April 1989, PDVSA and BP formed a joint venture, BP Bitor Ltd., to market Orimulsion® in Europe. In August 1989, Bitor America Corp. was formed for the marketing of Orimulsion® in North America and the Caribbean. Its offices are in Boca Raton, Florida. And, Bitor International Ltd. was formed to cover the marketing of Orimulsion® in the Far East, CIS countries, Scandinavia and North Africa. With Bitor's signing of long-term supply contracts in Europe, Japan, and Canada, it became necessary for Intevep to cede its rights to the Orimulsion registered trademark to Bitor.

Finally, Orimulsion® is the only liquid fuel that does not need refining, therefore, it has low energy consumption in its production. Long-term contracts assure customers a low cost and continuous supply. The cost of adopting an oil-fired station to burn Orimulsion® is much lower than building a new coal or gas plant. One final plus to note: Orimulsion® is shipped in conventional tankers, and an oil spill will be minimized since this water-based fuel will *disperse* readily in water, with the bitumen droplets suitable for marine microbial digestion.

For Intevep, Orimulsion® is a badge of honor. It has developed the technology to enable Venezuela to exploit its whale of a Belt. *And, Intevep is now developing the second and third generations of Orimulsion!*

Dr. Franzo Marruffo, one of the IVIC core of researchers, heads the Emulsion Technology Program, whose researchers developed the second and third generations of Orimulsion. In May 1990, work on the **second generation** was started, and in February 1991, a 750 b/d plant commenced operation in Lagoven's Cerro Negro sector. At the end of 1992, a new *25,000 b/d plant* was scheduled to begin operating.

In *second generation Orimulsion*, downhole emulsification is eliminated and bitumen is produced by dilution. This Orimulsion is *80% Orinoco®* to *20% water*, and is known as **EVC-80/20** (Emulsion de Viscocidad Controlada). This Orimulsion has a potential for gasification, can be used in a combined fuel cycle, is environmentally friendly, has no ash (like coal), and everything is burned! No water is needed to inject in combined fuel cycle, because Orimulsion already has water. It also works as a scavenger, mixing the residue of other fuels.

And what the *third generation Orimulsion* will offer is the final breakthrough, after which, there will be no need to develop more technology for Orimulsion. This would be the *Clean Emulsion*. Third generation Orimulsion will *eliminate sulfur*! And, this technology could also be used in refineries for residues. Hercilio Rivas has the patents for the new generation Orimulsion, along with Gustavo Nunez.

Until the final breakthrough that will eliminate sulfur in Orimulsion, Intevep has developed a patented process called **Promisox** ™, which is an SO_2 emission control technology. This flue gas desulfurization process was invented to compliment Orimulsion and clean up its emissions. *Promisox*™, the process, and *Promisorb*™, the active sorbent material that is used, were to be commercially marketed late in 1992, under a joint venture between Intevep and Energy and Environmental Research Corp.

(EER), of Irvine, California. Intevep began the development of this new process, which it owns, in 1989, with EER. Promisox™ removes sulfur from combustion gases not only in Orimulsion®, but in coal and fuel oil, as well.

Brigido Natera (now deceased), when he was President of PDVSA, gave a speech before the United Nation's UNITAR Conference on Heavy Oil and Tar Sands, in Long Beach, California, in July 1985, where he concluded by saying:

> I recall that an Oriental philosopher once said that all prediction is hazardous, especially with reference to the future, but I know I am on safe ground when I say that heavy oil is undoubtedly destined to be the liquid hydrocarbon of the Twenty-first Century, and beyond.

And Venezuela, besides having the largest heavy oil reserve in the world, is the country that knows the most about heavy crude oil and bitumen. Petroleos de Venezuela, thanks to Intevep and Lagoven, and through its affiliate Bitor, is stepping into the world electric power generation market. In the twenty-first century, the world will have a new fuel source for its production of electricity. Who would have believed, that the Orinoco whale would one day illuminate homes and businesses, and power the factories in the far reaches of the world? An old pioneer knew.

CHAPTER VI

INTEVEP'S PLACE IN VENEZUELA AND THE WORLD

I n Venezuela, there was no research in petroleum when the industry started in the nineteenth century. Manuel Pulido and his associates in La Petrolia, in the mountainous state of Tachira, sent Pedro Rincones to Pennsylvania, in 1879, to spend a year studying the new oil industry. It was Rincones' knowledge, acquired in the United States along with Venezuela's first oil rig purchased for $4,000, that formed the basis for the development of Venezuela's first small field and refinery, at La Alquitrana.

After 55 years, the little company, with offices in San Cristobal, Tachira, and in Caracas, folded at the same time that Venezuela was beginning to have its first oil boom, in the 1930s. The boom occurred after foreign oil companies entered Venezuela and obtained large concessions, in the 1920s. The Andinos who found oil in Tachira did so because there was an oil seep - a *mene*. They were pioneers, but not speculators or risk takers on the grand scale, and their means were modest. Above all they were coffee planters. They did not become wealthy through oil production.

In the twentieth century, some of the foreign oil companies did set up small laboratories in Venezuela. However, it took a 100 years before a first class research petroleum center was set up and funded by the oil industry in Venezuela. It was founded because some farsighted Venezuelans knew it was essential. As seen in earlier chapters, Intevep did not spring forth easily. It has at times been a battlefield — sometimes in the trenches, at other times with a rocket or two — but it has always been favored with some of the best researchers in Venezuela, because it is the *only one* in industrial oil research.

By 1987, Intevep's personnel accounted for 3% of the total personnel of PDVSA's affiliates. Out of the 708 people employed at Intevep, 97 had Ph.D.s, and 165 had Masters degrees. Technical assistance contracts had declined to only $55 million for the industry. (In 1988, the CATs declined to $39 million.) However, with the addition of the petrochemical industry, there was an additional $35 million in technical assistance contracts for Pequiven, in 1987. Intevep obtained 34 patents and 16 trademarks, and applied for 74 new patents, in 1987. By comparison, Exxon received around 300 patents, Shell received 200, and Elf Aquitaine 20 patents. Interestingly, both Exxon's and PDVSA's percentage of R & D investment in 1988 was 0.69% of their sales, whereas Shell's was 1.16 percent.

What a long way Intevep had come in *less than ten years*! from ground breaking at Villa Pignatelli in late 1976, and the arrival of the IVIC group of researchers in July 1978. One of the researchers at Intevep gave the author the following poem.

> We the unwilling
> Led by the unqualified
> Have been doing the unbelievable
> For so long, with so little
> That now we attempt
> The impossible with nothing.

One can only add that ironic humor is the dissimulation of wisdom.

Now, when researchers leave Intevep, they either go into private industry at higher salaries, or they go to research centers abroad. One is impressed by the dedication of the fine researchers who stay, for they do not enjoy special perks, or the deserved recognition from most of the industry. Once again these scientists are the unsung heroes. The parent holding company has no men at the top who were formerly in scientific research, therefore, at the top of the pyramid there is little understanding of scientific research: of how research is conducted, or how long a research project may take before, or if, it has results. This is a real dilemma for Intevep.

The setting for research is ideal. As one U.S. visitor described it: "Intevep's center in Los Teques is like a campus." By funding the research, *and* by allowing researchers the necessary freedom of time, unencumbered by the rigid company norms and bureaucracy, the Venezuelan petroleum and petrochemical industries will realize more breakthroughs in products and technology.

Andrei Sakharov in 1987, summarized the responsibilities of a scientist in the world: "Helping to preserve the peace, promoting scientific progress in a safe manner, furthering trust and openness in society, and defending victims of injustice. Science cannot be disconnected from life — the purpose of knowledge is to serve humanity."

But how do you recruit new scientists and researchers? It is often forgotten that a researcher has spent additional time *and* money in getting additional degrees in order to gain the needed knowledge **and** credentials for admission to a credible institution. By doing so he loses ground economically, but he gains in mobility! More than ever "science cannot be disconnected from life," and today, the good scientist is in demand, particularly in the West. The problem Intevep faces is who is going to do the research in the future? It now has wonderful new facilities to work in, but the men from IVIC are moving on: moving into administrative work, retiring, or moving into the private sector. How does Intevep recruit a Ph.D. with the needed credentials? In recent years, salaries in the Venezuelan petroleum industry have not kept up with those in the private sector, for there is a growing deficit as the government plucks and squeezes the Golden Goose — the petroleum industry!

In an effort to recruit and keep researchers, Intevep recently started three training programs. The first is a basic training program. The second is a strategic reserve, i.e., for those on a fast track. And the third is called, "challenge with a future" (Reto Con Futuro), whereby in five years Intevep will train 100 Ph.D.s, to do research. Under this program, 25 researchers were already studying abroad for their Ph.D.s, in 1992.

Intevep's Accomplishments and Plans

And what have the men and women researchers at Intevep accomplished? Plenty! In addition to the breakthroughs and accomplishments already mentioned in previous chapters, the following accomplishments should give an indication of how Venezuela has profited from the oil industry's investment in Intevep.

The following are the trade marks for some of Intevep's commercial products. The first three products are new catalysts for refining, in response to new and expanding conversion requirements and enforced environmental laws. The high content of sulfur, metals and nitrogen in Venezuela's heavy crudes presented a need for developing new refining processes, *or* revamping old ones, *and* developing natural catalysts with lower production costs, and synthetic catalysts as another alternative. **INT-R1** is a catalyst used in hydrotreating high-metal content *residuals.* **INT-FCC-1** is a catalyst for catalytic cracking of high-metal content *fuels.* **INT-GOV-10** and **20** are catalysts for hydrocracking in high content sulfur and nitrogen vacuum *gas oil* to produce middle distillates.

VRS is a subsoil pump for high viscosity crudes, which replaces the seat and ball travelling valve in regular rod pumps with a modular interchangeable assembly consisting of four parts. Used in drilling directional wells, **Forceliner** is a line of centering guides for downhole production equipment. It basically is a steel alloy bar with wheels fixed along its length. It is fully compatible with any brand of commercial sucker-rods, polished bars and pump draft-rods because Intevep has developed this technology in two versions: for sucker rods; and for the polished bar, and the draft rod, of the pump. All these products work more efficiently than those they replace, as well as outlast them, and reduce operating costs.

The above mentioned inventions are in addition to Imulsion® and Orimulsion®, which led to the formation of a new affiliate, Bitor, as well as Promisox™, all of which were covered in the previous chapter on the Orinoco Belt. Previously mentioned, in the section on patents, are HDH™, HHC™, and Coflow™, which offer new technologies to enable greater and fuller development of the Orinoco Belt, as well as other extra-heavy crudes.

In 1985, Intevep listed its most important projects in the following order: offshore OCS studies; geological studies of the Orinoco Belt; evaluation of technologies to upgrade heavy crudes; developing a technology to upgrade heavy crudes; evaluating and developing catalysts; developing and adapting the most resistant and efficient subsoil pumps; and studies of the uses of coke from heavy, high-metal crudes. They have obviously succeeded quite well.

With their *"Plan 2000"* produced in 1988, and now with the new *Master Plan 1991-2000* with further details of their goals for the year 2000, Intevep continues to carefully plan for the future. Since the first three Master Plans in 1975, 1977 and 1982 were produced, most of the installations have been built and the projects carried out. In 1991, the two large lab/offices, Sur 1 and Sur 2, were finished, thereby concluding the last of the major building projects.

In addition to the Master Plans, Intevep had several Corporate Plans, e.g. the above mentioned "Plan 2000," as well as corporate five-year plans, which are reviewed every year. Under these plans a diversity of research was spelled out. New research areas would include coal. And other areas of research would be increased, e.g., gas and oil engineering, combustion, petrochemicals, specialized information, chemistry of petroleum, and environmental engineering. Work with Palmaven and Carbozulia would be initiated. There would be increased commercialization of services and technologies developed at Intevep.

In research in petrochemicals, Intevep should help Pequiven move into specialized petrochemicals, which produce the highest profits, versus commodity petrochemicals, which are the feedstock petrochemicals and therefore produce less profits.

With the new emphasis on the environment and ecology, Intevep, in 1991, created the new *Division of Ecological and Environmental Research*. The new division was needed because of international environmental regulatory actions and the need for the development of cleaner technologies, and to assist, or improve, environmental conditions where the industry has operations in Venezuela. Venezuela has had an Environmental Law since 1976; and since April 1992, Venezuela has a fearsome Penal Law for the Protection of the Environment.

The division has four technical sections: Environmental Evaluation; Ecology; Control Technologies; and Environmental Regulations. The Environmental Evaluation section will utilize satellite images and remote sensing to complement techniques already in use. Some of the important environmental studies that Intevep and the Ecological Division are carrying out are on the Bolivar Coastal Fields of Lake Maracaibo.

In 1982, Maraven and Lagoven requested that Intevep conduct *studies on subsidence and compaction* on the *eastern coast of Lake Maracaibo*. For more than 60 years land surface subsidence has been observed along the eastern coast where the oil industry has operations. After discovering the giant Lagunillas oil field in 1926, Gulf Oil stopped drilling activities for several years, and its Mene Grande, along with Lago and Shell, in the late 1920s jointly built a large dike to protect their camps from the waters of Lake Maracaibo. *Half of Venezuela's total 44 billion barrels of produced oil* came from just *three* of the Bolivar Coastal fields, i.e., Lagunillas has produced over 11 billion barrels, Bachaquero (1930) 6.6 billion barrels, and Tia Juana (1928)
4.1 billion barrels. These 22 billion barrels of extracted oil have caused a serious subsidence problem in the area. Some of the land area over Lagunillas has dropped 5 1/2 meters! Within these subsidence basins, called "polders," a major pumping system has been built to transport rain water and runoff to Lake Maracaibo. The Eastern Coast of Lake Maracaibo (COLM) has 30 pumping stations, which not only pump rain water over the dike but they pump the water of several rivers that have their exit to Lake Maracaibo blocked by the dike. The coastal dike is 47 kilometers long, the internal dike is 59 kilometers, the drainage channels are 490 kilometers, and pumping capacity is 55 million b/d.

With a parallel study, sponsored by PDVSA, on the possibility of occurrence of compaction and subsidence in the extra-heavy oil reservoirs of the Orinoco Belt, Intevep, in 1983, combined the two projects. The Compaction and Subsidence research and development program was the first Intevep study designed to be implemented under a matrix scheme. This approach was subsequently taken to coordinate and carry out Intevep's main R and D multi-disciplinary efforts.

Basic research is approximately 5% of the total activity at Intevep. It is aimed at areas that will have long term application in the Venezuelan petroleum and petrochemical industry, and since 1986, when Carbozulia became an affiliate of PDVSA, in coal, too. It is sometimes carried out with a foreign market in mind, e.g. the HHC™ refining process will meet U.S. environmental desulfurization requirements for diesel fuels, under the Clean Air Act of 1990. The HHC™ process is a deep hydrogenation process comprised of two reaction stages using Intevep catalysts. HHC™ has high

flexibility, high quality by-products, and optimum catalyst utilization —
and is now commercial. Operating costs for HHC™ will be less than other
deep hydrogenation processes. Aires Barreto, the General Manager of the
Refining and Petrochemical Division, was in charge of the development of
this refining process.

Intevep's basic research is often started under *contract*, or technology
cooperation agreements with other research centers. For example,
Orimulsion commenced with an agreement with the Venezuelan
University of the Andes and with BP Research International, to study ways
of producing and transporting extra-heavy crudes. Orimulsion research,
thus, commenced with the collaboration of the British; and HDH develop-
ment occurred with the collaboration of the Germans — under the
Venezuelan-German Agreement of 1978, between the Ministry of Energy
and Mines and the West German Ministry for Science and Technology.
(From this agreement was born PDVSA's "internationalization," the Veba
Oel/PDVSA joint venture of Ruhr Oel, in 1983, and other projects.)
Intevep also signed *cooperation agreements* with: the French Institute of
Petroleum (IFP) in 1980; A B Nynas Petroleum (1987); and Veba Oel.

In 1983, Intevep had *technology agreements* with the U.S.'s DOE,
Canada's AOSTRA, PetroCanada, Petrobras, IFP, the University of Tulsa,
HRI, Terra Tek, Christensen Diamond, and BEICIP. *PDVSA* has signed a
number of *agreements* with other countries that Intevep participates in,
such as: PetroCanada, U.S. Department of Energy, Brazil's Cenpes, and
Petrobras, the Mexican Institute of Petroleum, and Elf-Aquitaine.

In 1991, Intevep signed a number of important agreements with
Venezuelan universities, including Venezuela's flagship university, the
Universidad Central de Venezuela. (At the Central University, the disciplines of petroleum engineering and electrical engineering were not added
to the curriculum until 1944 and 1947, respectively. Geology was added
in 1940.)

The Intevep contracts, over the years, have helped to seed and develop the growth of research in Venezuela, not only in the national universities, but in engineering and specialized companies. This fact becomes
apparent by looking at just four years. From 1980 through 1983, the participation of foreign engineering firms with contracts to the Venezuelan oil
industry dropped from 84% to 35%, while that of Venezuelan engineering
firms rose from 16% to 65 percent.

Intevep's stature now allows it to help other institutions and oil companies in less developed countries. Intevep has *technical assistance agreements* with: STAATSOLIE in Surinam; the Ministry of Energy and Mines in Guatemala; Barbados National Oil Company; Ecopetrol in Colombia; and Trintoc in Trinidad.

The Belt and Venezuela's Oil Reserves

With the major concentration of research on the Orinoco Belt during the first 10 years, because it is Venezuela's greatest reserve of hydrocarbons, Intevep not only looked for a way to produce, transport, burn, and refine this extra-heavy oil, it had to *analyze the oil* from the Belt. In one year alone, Intevep analyzed 256 crude samples from the Belt. (The first time I visited Intevep, I saw stacks and stacks of barrels of oil from the Belt. The barrels had different colored tops to identify the oil and its source.)

Venezuela's *proven* crude reserves in 1992 were **62 billion barrels**. Around 30% of Venezuela's total oil reserves are condensates, and light and medium gravity crudes. The remaining 70% are heavy crudes, less than 14° API, which require the use of high conversion refineries to obtain large amounts of lighter products.

Venezuela is using *12° API gravity* as the divider between extra-heavy (below 12°) and heavy. Venezuela has **44%** of the **world supplies** of oil below 12° API versus 4% of conventional crude oil. Around 75% of the Orinoco Belt is 8-11° API gravity. This extra-heavy oil is in unconsolidated rock. Intevep had to *develop measurement technology* to measure the Belt, because it was not available.

Ian Bass, an English geologist formerly with Corpoven, has estimated that the Orinoco Belt would fit in Lake Maracaibo, i.e., the water in the Lake is in quantity the same as the oil in the Belt.

Thus, because the Orinoco Belt is Venezuela's greatest petroleum reserve it had to be developed, once the Venezuelan oil industry had the technology to make it economically feasible.

Juan Pulgar, in an interview for Agropet's book, *Hombres del Petroleo* (Men of Oil), explained that the projects for the development of the Oil Belt were not only important for Venezuela's future, but would also stimulate Venezuela's economy and engineering professions. He called this the multiplier of investments, and among the many consequences, agriculture would be revived. Mr. Pulgar currently is Managing Director of PDVSA's Strategic Association Unit, which is in charge of joint ventures for the Orinoco Belt.

The President of the *Strategic Association Unit*, Jorge Zemella, in a speech in Dallas (at SMU's ISEM conference), in May 1992, said, "Despite their heavy gravity, production of most Orinoco crudes is viable, because their costs are in the range of only $3 to $5 per barrel produced." And he added, "we are . . . seeking partners to produce, by the end of the nineties, 400,000 barrels of Orinoco crude for conversion." Later in his speech, he explained why PDVSA was seeking joint ventures *in* Venezuela. Under the 1991 Venezuelan Income Tax Law, PDVSA's operations "continue to be penalized with an 82% aggregate tax rate," while any joint venture associated with heavy oil or natural gas production would have a 30% rate. Thus, if PDVSA has a foreign partner to develop Orimulsion, it would be taxed at the 30% rate.

But Venezuela is also developing its new *reserves of light and medium crudes*. Here too, Intevep is assisting the industry. The giant *El Furrial Field*, in Monagas, in eastern Venezuela, discovered by Lagoven in 1985, has been the source of a number of studies by Intevep. The Venezuelans are drilling their deepest wells in this field, which has been extended from El Furrial, to Musipan-Carito-El Tejero play to the west, by Corpoven. Lagoven set a drilling record early in 1991, reaching a depth with development well 3X Boqueron of 19,524 feet. The Furrial-28 crude, 28° API gravity, 1.4% sulfur, was introduced to the international market in November 1989. At that time, eight wells were producing 80,000 to 100,000 b/d. Proven reserves are still being added, as stepout wells continue to be drilled, but the already known billions of barrels of recoverable light and medium oil will probably make these fields the largest in the Western Hemisphere since the discovery of Prudhoe Bay in Alaska, in 1968.

This being the case, and with Intevep's successful and profitable results in the Orinoco Belt in southern Monagas and Anzoategui, Intevep now has research efforts north of the Belt in the northern sector of these states — helping resolve some drilling and production problems.

Research was conducted in El Furrial to determine the effects of the heat of injected water in a well, as well as that of the water itself, in precipitating asphaltents and the formation of emulsions. These variables can affect injection, therefore, the efforts to maintain pressure in the well.

Intevep is engaged in a research project for El Furrial and Ceuta, in Lake Maracaibo, that is one of the oil industry's biggest and most persistent headaches, namely *asphaltenes*. Asphaltenes are organic deposits, which are complex polymers that separate and when conditions of temperature and pressure vary they *clog* pipelines, separation columns, equipment, and even the oil wells. The problem has been studied by Intevep since 1980, however, it now has high priority due to the importance of the El Furrial/Musipan fields. Once again, the results of this research can be extrapolated in other problem zones around the world, like the North Sea (Ula), Algeria, and California (Ventura).

The Intevep Women

This book has mentioned the names of men, because they were the Founders, the Presidents, and the ones in authority at Intevep. The author first became aware of the importance of the women at Intevep when given a list of the patents. The most important patents that Intevep has carry the names of women, too. Women now make up 28% of the researchers in basic research at Intevep. Overall, women make up 35% of the personnel at Intevep, and several have key administrative positions, like Laura Varela, Manager of Corporate Affairs, and Julieta Sanchez, Manager of Institutional Relations.

Mentioned earlier in the section under patents, was Dr. Magdalena Ramirez de Agudelo, a chemist who has 10 patents in catalysts, and who heads the Olefins Production Project. Also mentioned was Carmen Galarraga who shares four of Dr. Agudelo's catalyst patents. Dr. Agudelo in 1991, won CONICIT's National Prize for Technical Research for her work in catalysts.

Maria Luisa Chirinos, a young chemical engineer, has eight patents from her work on Imulsion and Orimulsion. She was nominated, along with Dr. Hercilio Rivas and Ignacio Layrisse, for the Royal Society Esso Energy Award for 1992, for Orimulsion®.

Dr. Beatriz Arias, who has worked with Dr. Roberto Galiasso on catalysts for the HDH™ and HHC™ refining processes, has six patents. With a

Ph.D. in Chemistry from Catholic University in Louvain, Belgium, she is one of the IVIC group that moved to Intevep with Dr. Barroeta. Also working with Dr. Galiasso on catalysts was Adelina de Salazar, who along with Dr. Galiasso was awarded the 1984-1985 IBM Prize for Science and Technology, for their research on heavy crudes and residuals.

Josefina Vitolo is a chemist, who is in charge of the section of Motor Lubricants and Additives, in Petroleum Products. She is one of the first women to work at Intevep, having been hired and sent to Italy in 1978, to study the area of lubricants and additives at ENI. Upon her return to Intevep, she helped design and set up the laboratories and train the personnel. One of the principal areas of research in this section has been additives, since Venezuela had to import the package of additives for its lubricants.

Martha Cerhalmi de Hazos arrived in Venezuela from Hungary when she was three. She is another chemist and was one of the IVIC group that formed the core of Intevep's research group in 1977. She is head of the Molecular Spectroscope section in the Department of Evaluation and Analysis, where she works on crude oil fractions. She is a first-class mass spectroscopist.

Dr. Kathleen Hurley de Octavio, who has her Ph.D. in Environmental Engineering, is credited with designing the computer system for the industry's oil spill contingency program in Puerto la Cruz. She has a Masters from MIT, and started working for Intevep after moving to Venezuela.

These women are representative of the Intevep women who have the credentials, and experience, and are making a contribution to Intevep and the industry. Before Intevep, IVIC gave Venezuelan women opportunities to do research. Just as it was for men, outside of medicine, research for women in Venezuela hardly existed before IVIC. With the new opportunities, the women scientists in Venezuela are making their contribution. And with their help, Intevep is collecting more prizes.

Mission Accomplished

 ach year, the recognition of Intevep's accomplishments continues to grow. In 1991, Intevep won the prestigious UNESCO Prize in Science, for its HDH™ refining process. Intevep is the company that PDVSA cannot afford to cut back. Its growth and development have contributed to the whole industry's growth — and it can do more and more because it now has the trained people and the facilities, which it did not have 15 years ago. In February 1992, Intevep opened its *Western Division* with headquarters in Maracaibo, Zulia. One of the founders of Intevep, Alejandro Villoria, was named the General Manager. Initially, the work of the Western Division will be in technical services, and later, research and development will be added.

Among developing countries, Intevep is really unique. No other member of OPEC has a research center like Intevep. And while Pemex (Mexico), Petrobras (Brazil), and YPF (The Argentine) have research centers, they have not advanced like Intevep, and YPF is considering closing its research center, for lack of direction.

The Founders of Intevep did it right! They set up the research laboratory. When Thomas Edison was asked on his 80th birthday in 1927, by a reporter, what he considered his greatest invention, Edison promptly replied: "The research laboratory." He understood that it was the organizational technology of the research laboratory that channeled the talents and energies of a team. Since the Menlo Park lab commenced in the mid-1870s, research laboratories have been created around the world. The lessons learned from Menlo Park are: thinking in terms of the whole system; learning from failed attempts; letting customer needs drive the system; a system of continuous improvement; and continuous learning! Edison's mother taught him that learning (exploring) could be fun.

In the Introduction to this book it was pointed out that there was a division between the Ancients and the Moderns, the profound opposition between Jerusalem and Athens, and the modern attempt to alter their relation. It was Leo Strauss, who found Machiavelli to be the fountainhead of modern thought and the initiator of the radical break between the Ancients (Plato and Aristotle) and the Moderns. Strauss set about restoring the belief that the truth is the important consideration in the study of the thinker — that *the truth is always*!

A totally different view of the nature of things is the essence of modernity. Strauss rejected the Modern view, e.g. of Nietzsche, that there is a single line of Western rationalism originating in the Ancients and culminating in modern science. Man's mind and the world have been transformed by science, and science rests on pre-scientific foundations which can no longer be seen by science. This is the problem of knowledge as

Strauss saw it — thought that proceeds without a return to the pre-scientific world is captive to contemporary beliefs. Strauss provided the bridge from modernity to antiquity. He said that only by the closest attention to the surface could one get to the core.

Whereas the Duke of Wellington was supposed to have said, "The battle of Waterloo was won on the playing fields of Eton," the Founders of Intevep will be remembered for creating the core for the development of Venezuela.

Selected Bibliography

Alfonzo Ravard, General Rafael, **7 Anos de Una Gestion**, Discursos y Declaraciones del Presidente de Petroleos de Venezuela. Caracas: Ediciones Petroleos de Venezuela, 1982.

Arreaza, Julio Cesar, **Petroleos de Venezuela Una Organizacion Eficiente y Productiva.** Caracas: Graficas Armitano, 1983.

Beaton, Kendall, **Enterprise in Oil, A History of Shell in the United States.** New York: Appleton-Century-Crofts, Inc, 1957.

Bruno Celli, Blas, **Imagen y Huella de Jose Vargas.** Caracas: Publicaciones Intevep, S.A., 1984

Calderon Berti, Humberto, **La Nacionalizacion Petrolera: Vision de un Proceso**. Caracas: Graficas Armitano, C.A., 1978.

Coronel, Gustavo, **The Nationalization of the Venezuelan Oil Industry**, From Technocratic Success to Political Failure. Lexington, Mass: D.C. Heath and Co., 1983.

Dedmon, Emmett, **Challenge and Response**, a Modern History of the Standard Oil Company (Indiana). Chicago: The Mobium Press, 1984.

Fuenmayor, Euro, **Hombres del Petroleo.** Caracas: Ediciones Agropet, 1983.

McDaniel, Robert W., with Henry C. Dethloff, **Patillo Higgins and the Search for Texas Oil.** College Station: Texas A & M University Press, 1989.

Martinez, Anibal, **Venezuelan Oil, Development and Chronology**. London: Elsevier Applied Science, 1989.

Moron, Guillermo, **Los Presidentes de Venezuela, 1811-1979.** Caracas: Meneven, 1980.

Nockolds, Harold, **The Engineers.** London: Shell Petroleum Company, 1949.

Roche, Marcel, **Mi Compromiso con la ciencia.** Caracas: Monte Avila Editores, C.A., 1987.

Vallenilla, Luis, **Oil: The Making of A New Economic Order -** Venezuelan Oil and OPEC. New York: McGraw-Hill Book Company, 1975.

Histories of Standard Oil Company (New Jersey):

Hidy, Ralph W., and Hidy, Muriel E., **Pioneering in Big Business 1882-1911**, Volume I. New York: Harper & Brothers, 1955.

Gibb, George Sweet, and Knowlton, Evelyn H., **The Resurgent Years 1911-1927**, Volume II. New York: Harper & Brothers, 1956.

Larson, Henrietta, M., and Knowlton, Evelyn H., and Popple, Charles, **New Horizons 1927-1950**, Volume III. New York: Harper & Row Publishers, 1971.

Wall, Bennett H., **Growth in a Changing Environment 1950-1972**, Volume IV. New York: McGraw-Hill Book Company, 1988.

Popple, Charles Sterling, **(New Jersey) in World War II**. New York: Standard Oil Company (New Jersey), 1952.

For **primary sources**, dozens of Intevep in-house reports and briefing reports were used, as well as reports and papers presented by researchers at Intevep. The in-house annual reports include: Plan de Actividades, Plan de Operaciones, Anuario Estadistico, and Informe Sobre La Situacion Financiera y Recuperacion de Costos de Intevep. And, among special reports were: Marco Ambiental en Investigacion Y Desarrollo; Venezuelan-German Agreement, Annex III, Joint Research & Development on

Venezuelan Heavy Crudes; Long Range Technological Planning Seminar: February 4-5, 1983 (Considerations for Research and Development Activities); as well as Intevep's publications: *Revista Tecnica*, and *Notivep*.

Other primary sources include:

Brossard, Jr., E.E., and West, J.W., "Resume of Geology of Northeastern Venezuela." March 1927.

Hedberg, Hollis, "Geological Reminiscences of my early years in western Venezuela," *Boletin - Sociedad Venezolana de Geologos*, No. 34 (December 1988), 70-78.

Landau, Ralph, and Rosenberg, Nathan, "America's High-Tech Triumph," *American Heritage of Invention & Technology*, (Fall 1990), 58-63.

Invepet, "Diagnostica Sobre Tranferencia Technologica de la Industria Petrolera," Caracas, 1975, 239 pages.

Invepet, **Master Development Plans: 1975; 1977; 1982; 1991-2000.**

Many of the founders and researchers that the author interviewed supplied other primary sources, e.g., government Decretos.

APPENDIX

Intevep's Researchers and their Patents

I n November 1992, Intevep had a ceremony to honor 120 of its researchers and placed their names on a giant mural on the large exterior wall outside the entrance to the Intevep library building. Along side of each name was the number of patents that they had received, a total of 270 patents up to 1992. Their most important inventions, like Imulsion®, HDH™, HHC™, and Coflow™, and the prizes they had won, were listed on the mural. The following are the names of the inventors on the Intevep mural:

Inventors that received patents up to 1990:

Magdalena de Agudelo	(9)	Julio Krasuk	(8)
Jaime Almeida	(1)	Humberto Kum	(4)
Simon Antunez	(1)	Rafael O. Hidalgo	(2)
Luis Aquino	(3)	Juan Hurtado	(1)
Beatriz Arias	(6)	Donald Huskey	(1)
Jose Belandria	(2)	Jose Larrauri	(3)
Jesus Betancourt	(1)	Mario Lattanzio	(1)
Humberto Betancourt	(1)	Ignacio Layrisse	(9)
Rafael A. Bolivar	(1)	Francisco J. Lopez	(1)
Karen Brandwijk	(1)	Maria A. Lorente	(1)
Maria I. Briceno	(1)	Juan Lujano	(5)
Jose Luis Calderon	(3)	Alexander Maitland	(2)
Pascuale Caprioli	(3)	Juan J. Manzano	(1)
Lante Carbognani	(1)	Niomar Marcano	(1)
Antonio Cardenas	(2)	Edmundo M. Marquez	(1)
Angel Carrasquel	(7)	Humberto Marquez	(2)
Ivan Cavicchioli	(2)	Rosa L. Marquez	(1)
Jesus Chacin	(1)	Franzo Marruffo	(1)

Javier Chavez	(1)	Nelson Martinez	(6)
Maria L. Chirinos	(8)	Roger Marzin	(3)
Manuel Correa	(1)	Alfredo Morales	(11)
Javier Cruz	(1)	Orlando Morean	(1)
Gabriel Diaz H.	(1)	Carlos Mota	(1)
Simon C. Flores	(1)	Alejandro Newski	(4)
Carmen Galarraga	(4)	Jean F. Novak	(1)
Roberto Galiasso	(19)	Gustavo Nunez	(2)
Juan Jose Garcia	(3)	Mirna R. de Ojeda	(1)
Wolfgang Garcia	(1)	Jacinto Pachano	(3)
Cebers Gomez	(2)	Jose M. Pazos	(1)
Alejandro Granado	(1)	Lirio Quintero	(4)
Emilio Guevara	(3)	Georgette Rahbe	(2)
Jose Guitian	(5)	Jeanny T. de Rincon	(1)
Euler Jimenez	(6)	Hercilio Rivas	(4)
Luis Rivas	(1)	Roberto Schemel	(3)
Olegario Rivas	(6)	Felix Silva	(2)
Mayela Rivero	(3)	Fernando J. Silva	(1)
Antonio Robles	(1)	Bruno Solari	(4)
Domingo Rodriguez	(12)	Alfredo Souto	(1)
Jesus Rodriguez	(1)	Maria T. Terrer	(1)
Joaquin Rodriguez	(1)	Amnon Vadasz	(8)
Jose V. Rodriguez	(2)	Carlos Valles	(1)
Otto Rodriguez	(3)	Leon Velasco	(2)
Daisy Rojas	(2)	Jose R. Velasquez	(5)
Evelyn Romero	(1)	Maria L. Ventresca	(1)
Jose A. Salazar	(7)	Terence B. Wright	(2)
Jose Salazar P.	(6)	Konstantin Zagustin	(2)
Pedro Salazar	(1)	Carlos Zerpa	(4)
Ramon Salazar	(3)	Geza N. Zirczy	(1)
Vicente Sanchez	(1)	Jon Zurimendi	(1)

Inventors that received patents in 1991

Magdalena de Agudelo	(1)	Jean-Francois Nowak	(1)
Luis M. Cabrera	(1)	Pedro Ortega	(1)
Jesus Chacin	(3)	Hercillo Rivas	(1)

Anderson Chaviel	(1)	Antonio Robles	(1)
Juan C. De Jesus	(1)	Domingo Rodriguez	(1)
Roberto Galiasso	(1)	Jose A. Salazar	(1)
Euler Jimenez	(1)	Jose Salazar P.	(1)
Ignacio Layrisse	(1)	Amnon Vadasz	(4)
Rafael Manzano	(1)	Dino Verona	(1)
Edmundo M. Marquez	(1)	Omar Yepez	(1)
Alfredo Morales	(1)		

Inventors that received patents in 1992

Jesus Chacin	(5)	Milagros de Newski	(1)
Victor Chang	(1)	Olegario Rivas	(1)
Jose Rafael Castillo	(1)	Domingo Rodriguez	(2)
Jose Carrazza	(1)	Hugo Rodriguez	(1)
Cebers Gomez	(1)	Rui Rodrigues	(1)
Marilu Stea de Liendo	(1)	Irene Romero	(1)
Alejandro Newski	(1)	Amnon Vadasz	(5)

Winners of the Creativity Prize

1988: Jesus Chacin
1989: Simon Gonzalez
      Reinaldo Monque
      Adriano Parisi

1990: Victor Chang
1991: Ricardo Prada
      Yilda Romero
      Edito Reyes

INDEX